2002

JANUARY
M	T	W	T	F	S	S
	1	2	3	4	5	6
7	8	9	10	11	12	(13)
14	15	16	17	18	19	20
21	22	23	24	25	26	27
(28)	29	30	31			

FEBRUARY
M	T	W	T	F	S	S
				1	2	3
4	5	6	7	8	9	10
(11)	12	13	14	15	16	17
18	19	20	21	22	23	24
25	26	(27)	28			

MARCH
M	T	W	T	F	S	S
				1	2	3
4	5	6	7	8	9	10
11	12	(13)	14	15	16	17
18	19	20	21	22	23	24
25	26	27	(28)	29	30	31

APRIL
M	T	W	T	F	S	S
1	2	3	4	5	6	7
8	9	10	11	(12)	13	14
15	16	17	18	19	20	21
22	23	24	25	(26)	27	28
29	30					

MAY
M	T	W	T	F	S	S
	1	2	3	4	5
6	7	8	9	10	11	(12)
13	14	15	16	17	18	19
20	21	22	23	24	25	(26)
27	28	29	30	31		

JUNE
M	T	W	T	F	S	S
					1	2
3	4	5	6	7	8	9
(10)	11	12	13	14	15	16
17	18	19	20	21	22	23
(24)	25	26	27	28	29	30

JULY
M	T	W	T	F	S	S
1	2	3	4	5	6	7
8	9	(10)	11	12	13	14
15	16	17	18	19	20	21
22	23	(24)	25	26	27	28
29	30	31				

AUGUST
M	T	W	T	F	S	S
			1	2	3	4
5	6	7	(8)	9	10	11
12	13	14	15	16	17	18
19	20	21	(22)	23	24	25
26	27	28	29	30	31	

SEPTEMBER
M	T	W	T	F	S	S
						1
2	3	4	5	(6)	7	8
9	10	11	12	13	14	15
16	17	18	19	20	(21)	22
23	24	25	26	27	28	29
30						

OCTOBER
M	T	W	T	F	S	S
	1	2	3	4	5	(6)
7	8	9	10	11	12	13
14	15	16	17	18	19	20
(21)	22	23	24	25	26	27
28	29	30	31			

NOVEMBER
M	T	W	T	F	S	S
			1	2	3
(4)	5	6	7	8	9	10
11	12	13	14	15	16	17
18	(19)	20	21	22	23	24
25	26	27	28	29	30	

DECEMBER
M	T	W	T	F	S	S
						1
2	(3)	4	5	6	7	8
9	10	11	12	13	14	15
16	17	18	(19)	20	21	22
23	24	25	26	27	28	29
30	31					

Free,
Strong
and
Rare

□ *Melissa McConnell 1998*

◯ = NEW MOON, PST

◯ = FULL MOON, PST

WE'MOON '02

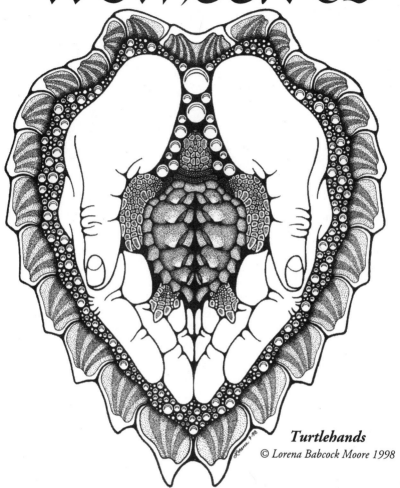

Turtlehands
© Lorena Babcock Moore 1998

GAIA RHYTHMS FOR WOMYN

PRIESTESSING THE PLANET

We dedicate WE'MOON '02 TO all Priestesses, ancient and new,
who tend the living flame of Spirit on the altar of the Earth.

published by
Mother Tongue Ink

WE'MOON '02: GAIA RHYTHMS FOR WOMYN AND WE'MOON '02 UNBOUND
© Mother Tongue Ink 2001

P.O. Box 1395-A
Estacada, Oregon 97023 USA
Phone: 503-630-7848 Fax: 503-630-7048
toll free: 877-O WEMOON (877-693-6666)
E-mail: matrix@wemoon.ws
URL: http://www.wemoon.ws

□ Candida Sea Blyth (cea) 1996

Priestessing the Planet

Crone Editor/Consultant: Musawa; **Creatrix/Editing Team:** Beth Freewomon, Bethroot Gwynn, Musawa, Meghan Garrity and Amy Schutzer; **Matrix Team:** Beth, Amy, Meghan, Cherie Smythe and Eagle

Front cover art *Gaia & Daphne* © Sandra Stanton 2000; back cover art *Sacred Thread Mandala* © Cynthia Ré Robbins 2000; See "Cover Notes" on page 189. Cover design © Meghan Garrity 2001.

Distributed directly by Mother Tongue Ink and by our other fine wholesale distributors: **USA:** Baker & Taylor, Bookpeople, Ingram, Koen, Lady Slipper, New Leaf, Northern Sun, Small Changes, Vision Distributors and Vision Works. **Canada:** Dempsey (Vancouver). **International:** Airlift (London), Bookpeople (Oakland, CA). A German edition of **We'Moon '02** is distributed by Neue Erde and Labyrinth Verlag (Braunschweig). To order directly from Mother Tongue Ink, see page 186.

Astro-data and ephemerides reprinted with permission from Astro Communications Services, Inc., P.O. Box 34487, San Diego, CA 92163-4487.

We'Moon '02 is printed with soy-based ink on acid-free, 85% recycled paper (min. 30% post-consumer) that is ECF (elemental chlorine-free). Using this paper instead of non-recycled paper saves about 166 trees, 72,600 gallons of water, 618 pounds of air pollution effluents, 48,000 kwh of electricity and 86 cubic feet of landfill space.

As a moon calendar, this book is recyclable; every nineteen years the moon completes a metatonic cycle, returning to the same phase, sign and degree of the zodiac. If you still have **We'Moon '84** you can use it again this year (**We'Moon '02** will be reusable in 2021)!

ISBN: 1-890931-09-8 **We'Moon '02** (with lay flat binding)
ISBN: 1-890931-10-1 **We'Moon '0** (with spiral binding)
ISBN: 1-890931-11-X **We'Moon '02 Unbound** (with no binding)

Printed and bound in USA.

Table of Contents

1. Introduction

II. Moon Calendar*

*Feature writers for the calendar pages of **We'Moon '02**: Astrological predictions by **Gretchen Lawlor**, holy day writing by various contributors, taoist herbal feature by Susan Raven Perri. **Disclaimer:** any herbal or astrological information herein should be used with caution, common sense and the approval of your health care practitioner, astrologer and/or other sources you trust.

III. Appendix

We'Moon: Gaia Rhythms for Womyn is more than an appointment book, it's a way of life! **We'Moon** is a lunar calendar, a handbook in natural rhythm and comes out of international womyn's culture. Art and writing by we'moon from many lands give a glimpse of the great diversity and uniqueness of a world we create in our own image. **We'Moon** is about

Keeping Watch
□ *Nadine C. Butterfield 2000*

womyn's spirituality (spirit reality). We share how we live our truth, what inspires us, how we envision our reality in connection with the whole earth and all our relations.

We'moon **means "women."** Instead of defining ourselves in relation to men (as in *wo*man or *fe*male), we use the word *we'moon* to define ourselves by our primary relation to the natural sources of cosmic flow. Other terms we'moon use are *womyn, wimmin, womon, womb-one*. **We'Moon** is a moon calendar for we'moon. As we'moon, we seek to be whole in ourselves, rather than dividing ourselves in half and hoping that some "other half" will complete the picture. We see the whole range of life's potential embodied and expressed by we'moon and do not divide the universe into sex-role stereotypes according to a heterosexual model. **We'Moon** is sacred space in which to explore and celebrate the diversity of she-ness on earth. The calendar is we'moon's space.

We'moon **means "we of the moon."** The moon, whose cycles run in our blood, is the original womyn's calendar. Like the moon, we'moon circle the earth. We are drawn to one another. We come in different shapes, colors and sizes. We are continually transforming. With all our different hues and points of view, we are one.

We'moon culture exists in the diversity and the oneness of our experience as we'moon. *We honor both.* We come from many different ways of life. At the same time, as we'moon, we share a common mother root. We are glad when we'moon from varied backgrounds contribute art and writing. When material is borrowed from cultures other than our own, we ask that it be acknowledged and something given in return. Being conscious of our sources keeps us from engaging in the divisiveness of either *cultural appropriation* (taking what belongs to others) or *cultural fascism* (controlling creative expression). We invite every we'moon to share how the "Mother Tongue" speaks to her, with respect for both cultural integrity and individual freedom.

Gaia Rhythms: We show the natural cycles of the moon, sun, planets and stars as they relate to earth. By recording our own activities side by side with those of other heavenly bodies, we may notice what connection, if any, there is for us. The earth revolves around her axis in one day; the moon orbits around the earth in one month ($29^1/_2$ days); the earth orbits around the sun in one year. We experience each of these cycles in the alternating rhythms of day and night, waxing and waning, summer and winter. The earth/moon/sun are our inner circle of kin in the universe. We know where we are in relation to them at all times by the dance of light and shadow as they circle around one another.

The Eyes of Heaven: As seen from earth, the moon and the sun are equal in size: "the left and right eye of heaven," according to Hindu (Eastern) astrology. Unlike the solar-dominated calendars of Christian (Western) patriarchy, the **We'Moon** looks at our experience through both eyes at once. The **lunar eye** of heaven is seen each day in the phases of the moon as she is both reflector and shadow, traveling her $29^1/_2$-day path through the zodiac. The **solar eye** of heaven is apparent at the turning points in the sun's cycle. The year begins with Winter Solstice (in the Northern Hemisphere), the dark renewal time, and journeys through many seasons and balance points (solstices, equinoxes and the cross-quarter days in-between). The **third eye** of heaven may be seen in the stars. Astrology measures the cycles by relating the sun, moon and all other planets in our universe through the star signs (the zodiac), helping us to tell time in the larger cycles of the universe.

Measuring Time and Space:
Imagine a clock with many hands. The earth is the center from which we view our universe. The sun, moon and planets are like the hands of the clock. Each one has its own rate of movement through the cycle. The ecliptic, a band of sky around the earth within which all planets have their orbits, is the outer band of the clock where the numbers are. Stars along the ecliptic are grouped into constellations forming the signs of the zodiac—the twelve star signs are like the twelve numbers of the clock. They mark the movements of the planets through the 360° circle of the sky, the clock of time and space.

Goddess Temple—Tarxien, Malta
¤ *Tracy Litterick 2000*

Whole Earth Perspective: It is important to note that all natural cycles have a mirror image from a whole earth perspective—seasons occur at opposite times in the Northern and Southern Hemispheres and day and night occur at opposite times on opposite sides of the earth as well. Even the moon plays this game—a waxing crescent moon in Australia faces right (e.g., ☾), while in North America it faces left (e.g., ☽). **We'Moon** has a Northern Hemisphere perspective regarding times, holy days, seasons and lunar phases.

Whole Sky Perspective: It is also important to note that all over the earth, in varied cultures and times, the dome of the sky has been interacted with in countless ways. *The* zodiac we speak of is just one of many ways that hu-moons have pictured and related to the stars. In this calendar, we use the tropical zodiac.

¤ *Musawa 1999*

HOW TO USE THIS BOOK

Useful Information about the We'Moon

Time Zones: All aspects are in Pacific Standard/Daylight Time, with the adjustment for GMT and EDT given at the bottom of each page. To calculate for other areas, see "World Time Zones" (p. 222).

Signs and Symbols at a Glance is an easily accessible handy guide that gives brief definitions for commonly used astrological symbols (p. 223).

Pages are numbered throughout the calendar to facilitate cross referencing. See Table of Contents (p. 5) and Contributor Bylines and Index (pp. 190–199). The names of the days of the week and months are in English with additional foreign language translations included (Esperanto, Swahili, German and Hawaiian).

Moon Pages mark the beginning of each moon cycle with an art-filled two-page spread near the new moon. Each Moon page is numbered with Roman numerals (ie., **Moon III**) and contains the dates of that Moon's new and full moon and solar ingress.

Month and Year at a Glance Calendars can be found on pp. 210–221 and p. 2. Month at a Glance pages include daily lunar phases.

Annual Predictions: For your astrological portrait for 2001, turn to Gretchen Lawlor's prediction for your sun sign. See "Astrological Predictions and Flower Essences for each Sign" (pp. 13–14).

Holydays and Herb Feature: There is a two-page holy day spread for all 2002 equinoxes, solstices and cross quarter days. These include descriptive writings and art by an assortment of contributors. You will find our herbal feature this year consolidated into one two-page article; see "The Five Elements" (p.25).

Planetary Ephemeris: Exact planetary positions for every day are given on pp. 204–209. These ephemerides show where each planet is in a zodiac sign at noon GMT, measured by degree in longitude.

Asteroid Ephemeris: Exact positions of asteroids for every ten days are given for sixteen asteroids in the zodiac at midnight GMT on p. 203. See "Asteroids" (p. 201) for more information.

Astrology Basics

Planets: Planets are like chakras in our solar system, allowing for different frequencies or types of energies to be expressed.

Signs: The twelve signs of the zodiac are a mandala in the sky, marking off 30° segments in the 360° circle around the earth. Signs show major shifts in planetary energy through the cycles.

Glyphs: Glyphs are the symbols used to represent planets and signs.

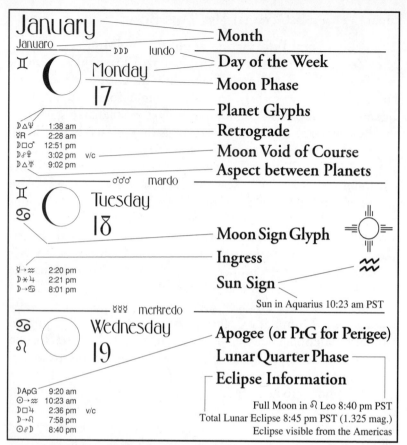

January
Januaro — ⅅⅅⅅ lundo
♊ Monday 17

Month
Day of the Week
Moon Phase

ⅅ△♆ 1:38 am
☿R   2:28 am
ⅅ□♂ 12:51 pm
ⅅ☌♀ 3:02 pm   v/c
ⅅ△♅ 9:02 pm

Planet Glyphs
Retrograde
Moon Void of Course
Aspect between Planets

— ♂♂♂ mardo —
♊ ♋ Tuesday 18

♅→♒ 2:20 pm
ⅅ✳♃ 2:21 pm
ⅅ→♋ 8:01 pm

Moon Sign Glyph
Ingress
Sun Sign

Sun in Aquarius 10:23 am PST

— ☿☿☿ merkredo —
♋ ♌ Wednesday 19

ⅅApG 9:20 am
☉→♒ 10:23 am
ⅅ□♃ 2:36 pm   v/c
ⅅ→♌ 7:58 pm
☉☍ⅅ 8:40 pm

Apogee (or PrG for Perigee)
Lunar Quarter Phase
Eclipse Information

Full Moon in ♌ Leo 8:40 pm PST
Total Lunar Eclipse 8:45 pm PST (1.325 mag.)
Eclipse visible from the Americas

Sun Sign: The sun enters a new sign once a month (around the 20th or so), completing the whole cycle of the zodiac in one year. The sun sign reflects qualities of your outward shining self. For a description of sign qualities see "Sun Signs" (pp. 15–17).

Moon Sign: The moon changes signs approximately every $2^1/_2$ days, going through all twelve signs of the zodiac every $29^1/_2$ days (the sidereal month). The moon sign reflects qualities of your core inner self. For descriptions see "Moon Signs and Transits" (pp. 18–20).

Moon Phase: Each calendar day is marked with a graphic representation of the phase that the moon is in. Although the moon is not usually visible in the sky during the new or dark moon, we represent her using miniscule crescent moon graphics for the days immediately before and after the *actual* new moon or conjunction. For more information about the moon, see related articles on pp. 21–23.

Lunar Quarter Phase: At the four quarter points of the lunar cycle (new, waxing half, full and waning half) we indicate the phase, sign and exact time for each. These points mark off the "lunar week."

Day of the Week: Each day is associated with a planet whose symbol appears in the line above it (e.g., ☽☽☽ is for Moon: Moonday, Monday, Luna Day, lundi, lunes). The names of the days of the week are displayed prominently in English with translations appearing in the line above them. Four languages (Esperanto, Swahili, German, Hawaiian) rotate weekly in this order throughout the calendar.

Eclipse: The time of greatest eclipse is given, which is not the exact time of the conjunction or opposition. Locations from where eclipses are visible are also given. For lunar and partial solar eclipses, magnitude is given in decimal form (e.g., 0.881 mag.), denoting the fraction of the moon's diameter obscured by the shadow of Earth. For total and annular solar eclipses, the duration of the eclipse in minutes and seconds is given. For more information see "Eclipses" (p. 200).

Aspects (□△⚹♂✳⚼): These show the angle of relation between different planets. An aspect is like an astrological weather forecast for the day, indicating which energies are working together easily and which combinations are more challenging. See "Signs and Symbols at a Glance" (p. 223) for a brief explanation of each kind.

Ingresses (→): Indicate planets moving into new signs.

Moon Void of Course (☽ v/c): The moon is said to be void of course from the last significant lunar aspect in each sign until the moon enters a new sign. This is a good time to ground and center yourself.

Apogee (ApG): This is the point in the orbit of a planet or the Moon that is farthest from Earth. At this time the effects of transits (when planets pass across the path of another planet) may be less noticeable immediately but may appear later on.

Perigee (PrG): This is the point in the orbit of a planet or the Moon that is nearest to Earth. Transits with the Moon or other planets when they are at perigee will be more intense.

Direct or Retrograde (D or R): These are times when a planet moves forward (D) or backward (R) through the signs of the zodiac (an optical illusion, as when a moving train passes a slower train which appears to be going backward). When a planet is in direct motion, planetary energies are more straightforward; in retrograde, planetary energies turn back in on themselves and are more involuted.

□ *Musawa and Beth Freewomon 2000*

PLANETARY DANCE 2002

This year's dance is dominated by several intense planetary formations as Saturn in Gemini moves into dynamic aspect with three of the four outer planets—Uranus, Neptune and Pluto. The more challenging configuration, the Saturn/Pluto opposition, peaks in May and June, joined sequentially by Sun, Moon, Mercury, Venus, Mars and an eclipse during that two month period. The more supportive aspects, the trine to Neptune and Uranus in Aquarius occur January–March (Saturn/Neptune) and August onwards (Saturn/Uranus).

How will this play out in our lives? The "reluctant metamorphosis" of the confrontation between Saturn/Pluto has been acute since first contact in August 2001 causing crisis in our belief systems. The discrepancies between what we have been taught to believe/our left brain logic (Saturn in Gemini) and what our body wisdom/intuition (Pluto in Sagittarius) is telling us ultimately forces a shift from existing linear thought to a more right brain wisdom on personal and political/social decision-making. A deeper awareness of right action replaces a sickness of spirit and a sense of emptiness and futility.

The trine aspects in air signs—Saturn in Gemini trine to Neptune and Uranus in Aquarius—provide a place for the intensity of the year to flow constructively. Saturn carries the potential to bring form to anything it touches. This trine to Neptune (first experienced June–July 2001, strongest January–March 2002) encourages us to give form to our fantasies, to blend inspiration with commitment to spiritual and compassionate action. Spiritual discipline becomes a necessary daily routine.

Saturn trine to Uranus encourages us to translate those thunderbolts of genius that we have increasingly experienced over the past six years into something tangible. Uranus leaves Aquarius in 2003; make sure the spark of individuation has rooted itself somewhere in your life. The house that holds Aquarius in your natal chart is your responsibility to transform, whether it be work, relationships, education, creativity, the way you raise your children . . .

Jupiter indicates doorways of opportunities; until August these appear through family or in or around your home. Take advantage of your generosity towards yourself. From August onwards, Jupiter in Leo brings a healthy increase in self-assurance and self expression—an invitation to the playful inner spirit to be more consciously present in your life.

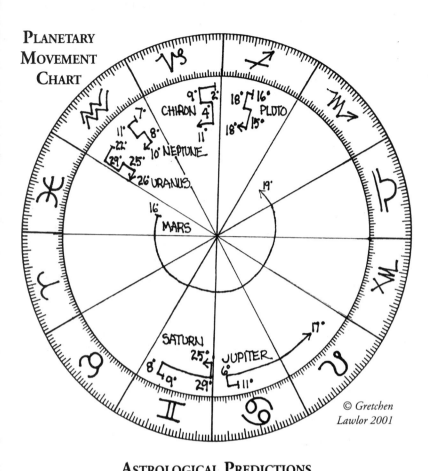

PLANETARY
MOVEMENT
CHART

© Gretchen
Lawlor 2001

ASTROLOGICAL PREDICTIONS
AND FLOWER ESSENCES FOR EACH SIGN

If you know your sun sign, you can find your prediction for this year on the calendar page where the sun enters that sign. (You will find Capricorn prediction on page 179.) Specific information may be gathered by reading predictions for both your sun sign as well as your rising sign—watch for repeated themes as well as any jangling dissonance. The predictions can provide an excellent navigational map for your own journey through the year.

Flower essences* provide support to help you weather well the

---

* I have chosen to focus upon FES and Bach essences as these brands are more easily found. These formulas may be available at many health food stores or you may order from me—$12.50 (postage paid) per formula; see my bio.

challenges and opportunties of the year ahead. One in particular, Hound's Tongue, may be useful for all signs in 2002 in its ability to facilitate balance between right and left hemispheres of the brain. Hound's Tongue marries reason with reverence and intuitive wisdom, the highest potential of the challenging Saturn/Pluto configuration, as well as nourishing the commitment to spiritual activism of the Saturn/Uranus and Saturn/Neptune trines.

Here is a specific support flower essence for each sign's journey through 2002:

Aries: Mountain Pride transforms dissatisfaction into positive energy for change.

Taurus: Sagebrush eases shedding of elements of life no longer appropriate for your true destiny.

Gemini: Cerato brings trust in inner convictions rather than the advice of others.

Cancer: Star of Bethlehem helps closure on old chapters of life.

Leo: Larkspur helps positive leadership and charisma within groups without feeling overburdened.

Virgo: Wild Oat assists in stepping into a perfect professional or public role.

Libra: Shasta Daisy helps you recognize the wise pattern of the whole within the many challenging parts of your life.

Scorpio: Borage releases grief and regret over past disappointments.

Sagittarius: Bleeding Heart to develop more freedom and objectivity in relationship.

Capricorn: Dandelion releases emotional tension held in the body.

Aquarius: Larch brings confidence to carry out your creative inspirations.

Pisces: Corn for grounded spirituality, for finding spiritual home.

SUN SIGNS
AND
TRANSITS

The sun pours out its energy through each sign's filter for one month a year. We feel its pulse in our daily life. The sun's sign influences our energy and colors our conscious world. Each of us holds our sun sign's medicine for the world.

© *Gwen Luptak 2000*

Aries (March 20–April 19): While the sun is in Aries we return to our Self, then reach for new beginnings. We have the courage to start over; in the process we may be headstrong and miss the subtleties. Decide what seeds to plant for this turn of the wheel.

An Aries embodies spring fire; she is erotic and independent, a primal rebel with revolutionary thought. She teaches us to stay centered and listen to our own calling.

Taurus (April 19–May 20): The Taurus sun sprouts the seed. Our ideas and creations begin to become solid and durable. This is a time to celebrate your body and the body of the Mother as we garden, sing, touch, make love, strengthen.

The Taurus woman embodies the strength to be soft and the heartbeat of the earth Mother. She makes her beliefs tangible. Comfort is her ritual. The Taurus challenge is to keep the material a sacred vessel, not an end in itself.

Gemini (May 20–June 21): While the sun traverses Gemini we learn the magic of communication as we cross-pollinate ideas and crops. Words weave connection. We search for inspiration.

Gemini eyes and nerves sing with electricity. She translates—from one friend to another or from one culture to another. Gemini challenges are to keep heart and nerves connected and to see through a problem, not just change the subject.

Cancer (June 21–July 22): While the sun swims through moon-ruled Cancer we learn the grounding magic of our home, our shell, our temple's hearth. To nourish body and soul we explore work with our chosen family, homeland and what makes us feel safe in the world.

Our moon womon is the guardian of the hearth, heart and culture. Their good minds and unusual memory all work as servant to the heart, their moods a source of wisdom. The Cancer challenge can be to let go, compost, explore.

Leo (July 22–Aug. 22): Life is a circus while the sun is at home in Leo—celebrate the ripening of the fruits of your plants and your creativity, passion and plans.

Leo can make a celebration out of any situation—why live a boring life. We gather around her as we gather around a bonfire. In that golden glow, all comes alive. Her challenge is to listen deeply and call people together for good reason.

Virgo (Aug. 22–Sept. 22): While the sun works its way through Virgo we bring in the harvest. It is time to sort our life, listen for new patterns and draw blueprints. Our thoughts turn inward and practical as we plan how to manifest the next stage of our dream.

Virgo harvests and sorts the wheat from the chaff. She is a healing force as long as she trains her vision to the harvest. Her challenge is to not get stuck on the chaff.

Libra (Sept. 22–Oct. 23): While the sun dances through Libra, meditate on relatedness; bring your life and loves into balance. Infuse beauty into your world. It's time to explore the Libran principle—where there is justice, there is peace.

Libra looks for engagement with equals. She offers kind respect, a steady eye and wants to bring balance to our world and all our relations. Her challenge is to seek internal balance.

Scorpio (Oct. 23–Nov. 21): While the sun burrows into Scorpio we prepare for winter's hibernation. It is time to bring our focus inward, concentrate on the mysteries and grow stronger as we face our fears.

A Scorpio is a deep well, a mystery and a detective. She knows nothing is simple. She is more interested in transformation than security. Sexuality is powerful magic to Scorpio. Her challenge is to balance her formidable focus with a broader horizon.

Sagittarius (Nov. 21–Dec. 21): While the sun travels through Sagittarius it's time to give thanks for the harvest. Let your restlessness take you anywhere unexplored—new friends, unfamiliar ideas or foreign soil.

Sagittarians live in the big picture. "Don't fence me in" is their theme song. They can speak to anyone. The Sagittarian challenges can be patience with slower mortals and learning to trust connection rather than a geographic cure.

Capricorn (Dec. 21–Jan. 20): With the sun in Capricorn, we are renewed by tradition and set our intentions for the year ahead. The Capricorn symbol is a sea-goat: she takes vision from the bottom of the oceanic dreamworld and walks it to the mountaintop.

Capricorns have backbone and help us see structure, form and practicality. She benefits from time alone, but without isolation. She needs goals she believes in—mountain goats aren't comfortable on flat land.

Aquarius (Jan. 20–Feb. 18): While the sun moves through Aquarius we dance with our politics and dialogue with our culture. It is time to find like minds and build strange alliances.

The Aquarian understands community. She holds the circle open for us. Innovation is her magic. She can be hypersensitive to the rules—breaking some and unusually bound by others. Her challenge is to build intimacy with herself first and then others.

Pisces (Feb. 18–March 20): While the sun courses through Pisces we soak it all up, listen to our dreams and ask where compassion will summon our actions in the year ahead.

Pisces feel the web that interconnects all life. Her dreams can hold the vision for all of us and our potential. Pisces are compassionate, intuitive mystics. Her challenge is to build a sound container to hold her dreams and keep her sensitivities intact. *© Heather Rowntree, 2000*

MOON SIGNS AND TRANSITS

The moon speaks directly to our spirit. It describes the daily pulse and the emotional matrix we walk through. As the moon changes sign every 2^1/$_2$ days, the filters on our inner world change. Let the garden be a metaphor for any project you want to nourish. Our own moon sign indicates our personal, spiritual lineage and our emotional prime-directive.

Moon Mother Divine
□ *Nadine C. Butterfield 2000*

The **Moon in Aries** asks us to wake up and remember who we truly are, even if it bothers those we love or work for. Tempers, tears and passions run hot. It's a great time for digging new beds, moving boulders, weeding or pest removal, but put a hold on planting. The Moon in Aries womon searches for fire, fierce independence and her own voice. She may need to learn patience and cooperation. She appreciates our fire.

The **Moon in Taurus** asks us to discover what nurtures us and how to grow deeper roots. We can almost feel the mud oozing between our toes, awakening our senses and sensuality and growing our stubbornness. It is time to cultivate our material resources, our homes and our body. Plant anything you want to grow strong and fertile. The Moon in Taurus womon searches for stability and sensuality. She may need to learn mobility. She offers us comfort, beauty and solid presence.

The **Moon in Gemini** quickens our nervous system. Build a web of understanding—network, absorb new information. Speak to your plants, trim, but avoid planting. The Moon in Gemini womon wants to understand, she lives and breathes communication. She may need to learn to honor stillness and concentration. She translates for us, questions us.

With the **Moon in Cancer** our feelings take the lead. Cancer encourages the wisdom rising out of our oceanic unconscious through moods and feelings. Ground in the magic of our home as a temple. Ask what needs protecting and feeding. Plant, fertilize and water your garden. The Moon in Cancer womon searches for what nurtures her soul and the world's. She may need to learn to carry her security with her. She respects our deepest feelings, eases our past fears.

With the **Moon in Leo** we have the guts to be visible and bring culture to life. In your garden or life, arrange, glorify and weed the extraneous so your star can shine, but don't plant or fertilize. The Moon in Leo womon came here to dramatize and ritualize her world. She may need to learn to find the sacred in the mundane. She offers us celebration and fascination and honors our self-expression.

The **Moon in Virgo** asks us to consider what needs healing, what needs composting. It's time to study, learn, train, organize and turn our compassion into pragmatic action. Don't get stuck in your head. Weed, prune, ammend your garden with nutrients and companion planting. Plant and care for medicinal herbs. The Moon in Virgo womon came here to diagnose and heal her soul and the world's. She needs to learn to celebrate the beauty in each of us. She offers us practical compassion and ancient wisdom.

Moon in Libra highlights the magic of the dance of inter-relatedness—friendly, romantic and searching for a way to connect. Libra asks us to treat those around us as equals and make sure our politics and art, our lovemaking and our networks integrate. Tend to the beauty of the garden, cultivate, but don't plant. The Moon in Libra womon came here to feel the beauty in cooperation. She may need to learn to hear her own voice under conflict. She offers us bone-deep kindness, mediation and justice.

With the **Moon in Scorpio**, dig deep. Scorpio weaves the visible and invisible worlds together. We see through and into the roots. Direct this energy away from obsession and towards creation. Sexuality can be potent, musky. Dig in your garden, plant roots, feed the soil and compost. The Moon in Scorpio womon came here to find herself in solitude first and then through transformative action with others. She may need to learn flexibility. She offers us a fearless guide to the inner worlds as she midwifes all transitions.

Moon in Sagittarius brings out our inner-Artemis; we need to roam, to explore in body and in soul. Our curiosity intensifies. Check out untraveled territory and connect with the organic world. Have a long talk with the animals in your garden. Work the soil but hold off on the planting. The Moon in Sagittarius womon came here to explore. She needs to learn to hold still and work through a challenge. She offers us radical acceptance.

□ *Monica Sjöö 2000*

Moon in Capricorn brings planning magic and takes your ideas, giving them form and hope. We can tap into the inner wisewoman—ask how form, ritual, organization or tradition can serve. Trim, prune, plant slow-growing seedlings and make sure you and your garden have enough water. The Moon in Capricorn womon came here to accomplish and understand compassionate leadership. She may need to learn to respect other rhythms and to love herself, not just what she does. She offers us constructive determination and practical support.

The **Moon in Aquarius** expands our circles and offers the magic of collaboration; spirit and politics weave together. We can get too farsighted now and need to stay aware of others' feelings. Let go of assumptions and find new, unusual allies. A time to gather plants, mulch, prune and talk to your garden. The Moon in Aquarius womon came here to understand group dynamics. She may need to learn to be comfortable with emotional intimacy. She offers us a global perspective and collaboration.

With the **Moon in Pisces** we feel the world with compassion, heightened senses and strong imagination. We need quiet time in the temple or back under our covers to deal with sensory overload. A time to vision, listen to inner voices, creative juices and touch each other with new awareness. Plant, transplant, water, fertilize. Moon in Pisces womon came here to feel everything; she may need to filter impressions and find her deep strength. She offers us insight, imagination, and subtle, compassionate medicine while encouraging our vision. © *Heather Rowntree 2000*

LUNAR RHYTHM

Everything that flows moves in rhythm with the moon. She rules the water element on earth. She pulls on the ocean's tides, the weather, female reproductive cycles, and the life fluids in plants, animals and people. She influences the underground currents in earth energy, the mood swings of mind, body, behavior and emotion. The moon is closer to the earth than any other heavenly body. The earth actually has two primary relationships in the universe: one with the moon who circles around her and one with the sun whom she circles around. Both are equal in her eyes. The phases of the moon reflect the dance of all three: the moon, the sun, and the earth, who together weave the web of light and dark into our lives. No wonder so much of our life on earth is intimately connected with the phases of the moon!

On the following two pages you will find articles about the moon and her cycles that correspond to the chart below.

□ *Musawa 2000*

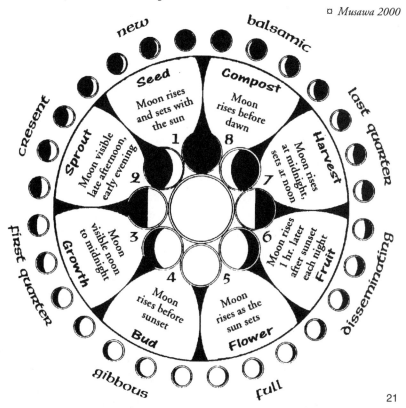

THE EIGHT LUNAR PHASES

As above, so below. Look into the sky and observe which phase the moon is in. Then you will know where you are in the growth cycle of each lunar month. The phase that the moon was in when you were born reflects your purpose, personality and preferences.

The **new moon** is like a SEED planted in the earth. We cannot see her but she is ready to grow, full of potential and energy for her new journey. We'moon born during the new moon are impulsive, passionate and intuitive. They are risk takers and pioneers.

The **crescent moon** is the SPROUT. The seed has broken through the earth and reaches up as she ventures from the dark, moist earth she has known. We'moon born during the crescent moon must break from the past to create their own destiny.

The **first quarter moon** is the GROWTH phase. Roots go deeper, stems shoots up and leaves form as she creates a new strong body. We'moon born during the first quarter moon live a full active life— old structures are cleared away providing room for new development.

The **gibbous moon** is the BUD of the plant, the pulse of life tightly wrapped, wanting to expand. For we'moon born during the gibbous moon, their talents lie in the ability to refine, organize and purify. They are seekers, utilizing spiritual tools as guides on their path.

She opens and blossoms during the **full moon** into the FLOWER, with the desire to share her beauty with others. We'moon born during the full moon enjoy companionship and partnership and desire to merge deeply. Fulfillment and illumination are their goals.

As we go into the darkening phase of the **disseminating moon**, we get the FRUIT of the plant's life cycle—the fruits of wisdom and experience. For we'moon born during the disseminating moon, life must have meaning, purpose. They enjoy sharing their ideas with others.

The **last quarter moon** is the HARVEST phase—the plant gives her life so that others may continue theirs. We'moon born during the last quarter have a powerful internal life of reflection, transformation. They can assume different roles while balancing their internal and external worlds.

The **balsamic moon** is the COMPOST phase, when the nutrients remain in the soil, providing nourishment for the next new seed. We'moon born during the balsamic moon possess the potential to be wise, insightful, understanding and patient. They are prophetic and unique.

◻ *Susan Levitt 2000*

WHERE'S THAT MOON ?

Why is the moon sometimes visible during the day? And why does the moon sometimes rise very late at night? The answers lie in what phase the moon is in, which reflects the angle between the sun and moon as seen from Earth. For each of the eight moon phases, the angle between the sun and moon progresses in 45° increments. Each phase lasts approximately 3–4 days of the moon's entire $29^1/_2$ day cycle.

The **new moon** (or dark moon) rises at sunrise and sets at sunset. Astrologically, the sun and the moon are in *conjunction*. Because the sun's light overpowers the nearby moon in the day, and the moon is on the other side of the earth with the sun at night, she is not visible in the sky at all.

The **crescent moon** (or waxing crescent moon) rises midmorning and sets after sunset. She is the first visible sliver of moon seen in the western sky in the late afternoon and early evening.

The **first quarter moon** (or waxing half moon) rises around noon and sets around midnight. Astrologically, the moon is *square* to the sun. She is visible from the time she rises until she sets.

The **gibbous moon** rises midafternoon and sets before dawn. She is the bulging moon getting ready to be full, visible soon after she rises until she sets.

The **full moon** rises at sunset and sets at sunrise. Astrologically, the sun and moon are in *opposition* (ie., opposite each other in the sky and in opposite signs of the zodiac). She is visible all night long from moonrise to moonset.

The **disseminating moon** is the waning full moon getting visibly smaller. She rises midevening and sets midmorning. She is visible from the time she rises almost until she sets.

The **last quarter moon** (or waning half moon) rises around midnight and sets around noon. Astrologically, the moon is *square* to the sun. She is visible from the time she rises until she sets.

The **balsamic moon** (or waning crescent moon) rises before dawn and sets midafternoon. She is the last sliver of moon seen in the eastern sky in the dawn and in the very early morning.

□ *Susan Levitt, Musawa and Beth Freewomon 2000*

THE YEAR OF THE HORSE

The year of the Horse begins on the new moon of February 11, 2002*. Powerful Horse has magical qualities, including the ability to fly. A white celestial cloud Horse was sacred to the compassionate Goddess Kwan Yin. Kwan Yin's white Horse flies through the heavens, bringing peace and blessings.

Horse year is a time of victory, adventure, exciting activities, surprising romances and fun. Decisive action, not procrastination, brings success. Energy is high and production is rewarded. On a global scale, expect world economies to become stronger and for industrial manufacture to rise. Or expect economic chaos or collapse, such as the San Francisco earthquake, World War One, the Great Depression and the Chinese Cultural Revolution that all began in Horse years. Under strong Horse's influence, there is no middle ground.

Wemoon born in Horse years (2002, 1990, 1978, 1966, 1954, 1942, 1930, 1918, 1906) are bright, open, cheerful, popular and fun-loving. Film, theater and most forms of entertainment inspire her. With her sunny disposition and natural charm, Horse finds people and crowds exciting and she loves parties. Her childlike innocence often attracts many friends. Horse is frank and dislikes hidden agendas. She will tell you what is on her mind.

In general, Horse can enjoy a carefree life. Usually she doesn't need to struggle in order to succeed and obtain the fine things life has to offer. Because Horse is an intuitive animal, the Horse wemoon follows her hunches. Her keen judgment and natural intuition often help her make the right decisions throughout her life.

Rebelliousness can be a difficult Horse trait. Because of her carefree nature, Horse needs ample room for self-expression, especially the fire Horse (born in 1966). When constrained by rules, proud Horse refuses to be corralled or tamed. Stay free Horse, stay free!

¤ *Susan Levitt 2001*

*Asian New Year begins the second new moon after Winter Solstice.

© Max Dashu 2001

THE FIVE ELEMENTS

The ancient Chinese tradition of healing and philosophy acknowledges the presence of five sacred creative forces in all living things. These Five Elements (Fire, Earth, Metal, Water and Wood) are inherent in nature and all her cycles. The sanctity of health and wholeness are closely connected to the harmonious balance of the Five Elements, in all beings and within the regenerative flow of life energies.

Water: In Chinese Medicine, the winter season is ruled by the Water element. In the body, the kidneys and bladder are ruled by Water as well. The Water element is connected to the root chakra of Eastern Indian tradition, and is grounded in issues of safety. An unbalanced Water element is evident in feelings of fear and paralysis or frozen will. Deficient Water follows overspent energy and is restored by tuning back into our inner knowing. Quiet and solitude are necessary in a regular way to maintain balanced Water. Balanced Water is manifest as feeling connected and protected, sitting in the lap of the Great Mother. Salty foods nourish the Water element, such as nutrient-rich seaweeds like dulse and wild Atlantic nori. Nutritive green tonics of nettle and chickweed help balance and build the Water element and assist healthy kidney function.

Wood: Spring sends up tender shoots from beneath the decaying mulch of autumn. Likewise, the Wood element rules the liver and the body's cleansing process of sorting pure from impure. Wood embodies the wisdom of knowing when to move and when to be still. Spring is an optimal time to nurture and tone the Wood element and boost liver function. Bitter herbs accelerate and support the inherent cleansing capacity of the liver, helping to clear the blood and process winter sluggishness. Nourish the Wood element with hepatic herbs: blessed thistle, dandelion, chickory and yellow dock roots. Eat early spring greens such as dandelion and sorrel to support the Wood element and internal spring cleaning.

Fire: Solar power concentrates in the summer months, a season of the Fire element. Fire governs the heart and circulation and is a conduit between heaven and earth. According to Chinese Medicine, this is a time for inspiration and creative flow, a union of spirit with matter. Balanced Fire manifests as joyful self-expression. A tranquil mind, clear senses and a robust complexion are all aspects of balanced Fire. Fire thrives on new ideas and activities and rules interpersonal communication. Love your inner Fire with "spicy" herbs like rosemary, holy basil and lavender. Use as teas, food, flower essences or essential oils to nourish and balance Fire. Support cardiovascular and circulatory health with horse chestnut and hawthorne.

Earth: The last surge of summer, early fall, is the season of the Earth element. In traditional Chinese Medicine the Earth element embodies sweetness and the summer's harvest. Earth rules the stomach and digestion and on a deeper level it represents how we digest our life experiences. Balanced Earth nourishes the inner caretaker and peacemaker. Earth seeks harmony and is nurtured by hearth and home. In this season of the Earth element, devote special attention to digestion. Provide herbal allies to nourish inner Earth and an appetite for all of life. Sweet herbs such as fennel, anise, and sweet basil are digestive tonics and restore the earth element. Drink nutritive sweet seed teas to balance inner Earth and reconnect with your trust in abundance.

Metal: The first frosts and crisp air of autumn bring clarity and this is the energy of the Metal element. Following traditional Chinese Medicine, Metal rules the lungs and the process of breathing. Metal carries the power of change and the ability to balance intimacy with isolation, attachment with surrender. Herbs with a pungent taste such as mullein and comfrey leaves nourish the Metal element and support respiratory health.

© Susan Raven Perri 2001

THE WHEEL OF THE YEAR: HOLY/HOLIDAYS

The seasonal cycle of the year is created by the tilt of the earth's axis, leaning toward or away from the sun, north to south, as the earth orbits the sun. Solstices are the extreme points (like new and full moon in the lunar cycle) when days and nights are longest or shortest. On equinoxes, days and nights are equal (like the light of the half moon). The four cross-quarter days roughly mark the midpoints in between solstices and equinoxes. These natural turning points in the the earth's annual cycle are the holidays we commemorate in **We'Moon**. We use the dates in the ancient Celtic calendar because it most closely approximates the eight spokes of the wheel of the year. As the wheel of this year turns, **We'Moon** features interpretations of the seasonal holydays by priestesses of past **We'Moons**—reprinted. The holy/holiday celebrations of many cultures cluster around these same times with similar universal themes:

Dec. 21: Solstice/Winter: the dwindling and return of the light—Kwanzaa (African-American), Soyal (Hopi), Santa Lucia (Scandanavian), Cassave/Dreaming (Taino), Chanukah (Jewish).

Feb. 2: Imbolc/Mid-Winter: celebrations, prophecy, purification, initiation—Candlemas (Christian), New Years (Tibetan, Chinese, Iroquois), Ground Hog's Day (American), Tu Bi-Shevat (Jewish).

Mar. 20: Equinox/Spring: rebirth, fertility, eggs, resurrection—Passover (Jewish), Easter (Christian), Festivals of the Goddess: Eostare (German), Astarte (Semite), Persephone (Greek).

May 1: Beltane/Mid-Spring: blossoms, planting, fertility, sexuality—May Day (Euro-American), Root Festival (Yakima), Ching Ming (Chinese), Whitsuntide (Dutch).

June 21: Solstice/Summer: sun, fire festivals—Niman Kachina (Hopi), Sundance (Lakota), Goddess festivals: Isis (Egypt), Litha (N. Africa), Yellow Corn Mother (Taino), Ishtar (Babylonian).

Aug. 2: Lammas/Mid-Summer: first harvest, breaking bread, goddesses of abundance: Green Corn Ceremony (Creek), Corn Mother (Hopi), Amaterasu (Japan), Hatshepsut's Day (Egypt).

Sept. 22: Equinox/Fall: gather and store, ripeness, goddesses: Tari Pennu (Bengal), Old Woman Who Never Dies (Mandan), Chicomecoatl (Aztec), Black Bean Mother (Taino).

Oct. 31: Samhain/Mid-Fall: underworld journey, ancestor spirits, Hallowmas/Halloween/Festivals of the Dead around the world, Sukkoth (Jewish harvest/wine festival).   ◻ *Musawa and Nell Wagenaar 2000*

Sources: *The Grandmother of Time* by Zsuzsanna E. Budapest, 1989; *Celestially Auspicious Occasions* by Donna Henes, 1996; and *Songs of Bleeding* by Spider, 1992

Introduction to the Theme: Priestessing the Planet

"To Priestess: to hold sacred space, be a conduit for spirit, tend to the elements of ritual; to exercise power wisely, catalyze the transformation of energy, call the people together to focus and facilitate, envision and inspire, empower, teach, and guide change on all levels."

—from the **We'Moon '02** Call for Contributions

We could never have imagined the challenge of "change on all levels" which we have had to meet in "priestessing" the **We'Moon '02**. In the early morning of February 18, 2001, (the dawning of the Sun in Pisces), the Main House at We'Moon Land, including the offices of Mother Tongue Ink, publisher of the **We'Moon** calendar, burned to the ground. No one was injured, but other damage was total. Computer systems, archives, art submissions accumulated through many years, thousands of copies of **We'Moon '01** and every piece of art and writing submitted for the **We'Moon '02** were destroyed. All record of the selections we had made was lost, along with hours of data input, editing and proofing of computer generated copy. All that work was consumed by Pele, the Goddess of Fire, in a roaring blaze. We are grateful that She spared the nearby trees, resident spaces . . . and our lives.

The Priestess card in the Tarot (Major Arcana card II) had been our guide for choosing the **We'Moon '02** theme. Now the fire threw us into urgent and magical priestess activity in order to re-birth the **We'Moon** from the ashes. Like the Sumerian Goddess, Inanna, **We'Moon '02** had been dismembered. In order to priestess this edition, we had to travel into the underworld of unconscious process to re-member her. With the technology gone, and the poems, stories, slides, prints destroyed, the four of us serving as the Creatrix had to dive deep into the ocean of memory, fishing for images and sentences which would help us recall the **We'Moon** pages we now saw only in our mind's eye.

A partial list of contributors, retrieved from the burnt-out fire safe, and a pile of charred wet release forms found in the ashes of the Main House, were the only clues we had for reconstructing the **We'Moon '02**. We had a taste of the kind of technological failures prophesied for Y2K and the turn of the new millenium. With our

28

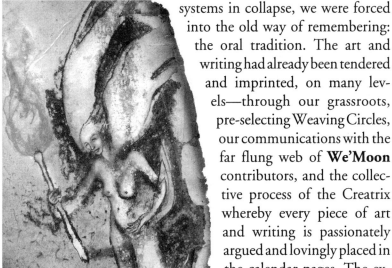

Salvaged "Fire Art"
© *Deborah Koff-Chapin 2000*

systems in collapse, we were forced into the old way of remembering: the oral tradition. The art and writing had already been tendered and imprinted, on many levels—through our grassroots, pre-selecting Weaving Circles, our communications with the far flung web of **We'Moon** contributors, and the collective process of the Creatrix whereby every piece of art and writing is passionately argued and lovingly placed in the calendar pages. The extensive interactions involved in creating **We'Moon** were all grist for the mill of memory, grounded in the magic of community, the well-spring from which **We'Moon** is created and recreated.

By the New Moon in Pisces, five days after the fire, we were creating sacred space in an old trailer on the land (formerly called Bertha, now Rebertha, our new office and community hub), conjuring magic to release the pain, learn the lessons and receive the blessings of the fire. By New Moon in Aries, the Matrix was hard at work contacting contributors to gather in the missing pieces we had recalled and reproducing the calendar pages on computers once again. The contributors were generous and forgiving in their responses. By New Moon in Taurus, the **We'Moon** Matrix was preparing the semi-final copy *again* . . . in time for weaving together a renewed tapestry that would almost be completed by New Moon in Gemini. The outpouring of love and support from wemoon here and all over the world held us in our labor as we midwifed this **We'Moon**.

When we chose the theme for **We'Moon '02**, we wanted to honor work that women are doing all over the world to heal and tend Mother Earth, to empower women and to make the world safer for all beings. We shaped the priestess word as a *verb*, in order to focus on women's activity, small scale or grand-gestured. The priestess is not only the one who conducts ritual, she is also the one who sweeps behind the altar (to use an image from a poem that was lost in the fire). She is not only the woman who takes visible leadership in the public eye, challenging exploitation and making waves that impact national and global policies, she is also the woman who makes quiet revolution mending the broken in everyday life, in her backyard, her neighborhood, her community.

"We invite you to share ways in which you priestess the planet. Life on earth is endangered on so many levels that the creativity of women is especially called forth for the transformations needed at this time. Who and what moves you to action? Who are the womyn you know whose work changes the world?"

—from the **We'Moon '02** Call for Contributions

Priestesses are women attuned to Spirit in ordinary life, dedicated to life-affirming values, extraordinary in a global culture driven by profit and disdain for biosphere survival. Priestesses can skip right over conventionally-drawn boundaries between the political and the spiritual, between art and politics, the personal and the global, worship and play. In traditional Tarot imagery, the High Priestess is often depicted between opposite pillars, holding keys to the gateway of Mystery that leads beyond duality. Her authority comes from her wholeness, drawing on the source of oneness rather than being drawn into opposition. Her sanctuary is the whole earth.

We'Moon '02 reflects the planet-wide range of priestess work. Womyn submitted art and writing that honors transformative activities of womyn from Mexico, Nepal, Afghanistan, Australia, India, Africa, China, Peru, North America, the British Isles. Women are saving trees, ancient traditions, seeds, cultural freedoms, sacred spaces and helping people in need. They are creating rituals that honor the body and life transitions. They attend to temples, plants, children; create poems, protests, prayers. There is sometimes anger in these calendar pages, sometimes grief, as women confront the devastations engineered by powerful institutions of social control and environmental pillage. There is celebration and reverence for the resilient, enduring forces of the natural world and for the creativity that women are bringing forward to clean up the mess that "Man" has made, to recreate a balanced, sustainable way of life for Earth and all beings.

This **We'Moon**, with its theme of the active priestess, provides inspiration for us to consider some more activist projects that could spin off from our work. Stirred by women in prison (to whom we send free **We'Moons**), we are imagining a network of spiritual practice/study groups for women behind walls. We are also interested in prospects for networking an international Women's Empowerment Corp. These ideas are examples of seed material for a new non-profit organization called We'Mooniversity, created by We'Moon Land members and community supporters in order to resource and expand the services offered to women through this womyn's land (now in its 29th year) and this calendar (now in its 22nd year). The fire that wiped out **We'Moon** headquarters has forcefully cleared the way for these expansions. The new, spacious Community Center-to-be will hopefully have facilities for workshops, retreats, gatherings, offices for priestess work we have not yet dreamed of... We invite your input, participation and support. See Resources on page 188 for projects referenced in the calendar as well as for more information on We'Mooniversity .

The names of the thirteen Moons incant ways in which womyn are priestessing the planet. We invite you to join in this sacred work with wemoon around the world.

Turtle Island Protectress
© *Katheryn Trenshaw 1996*

RETURN/RESIST
REMEMBER/REMIND
TEACH/GUIDE
RENEW/REBUILD
EMBODY/HEAL
MEDITATE/CREATE
MOTHER/NURTURE
CIRCLE/INVOKE
LIBERATE/EMPOWER
GRIEVE/PROTECT
MIDWIFE/TRANSITION
ALLY/COMMUNE
HONOR/EMBRACE

◻ *Musawa and Bethroot 2001*

Amazon Warriors of the Bronze Age
¤ *Monica Sjöö 2001*

I. RETURN/RESIST

Moon I: December 14–January 13

New Moon in ♐ Sagittarius: Dec. 14; Sun in ♑ Capricorn: Dec. 21; Full Moon in ♋ Cancer: Dec. 30

To Pele
Goddess of the Living Fire
© *Lilian de Mello 1997*

The Calling

Sisters, what if it is true? What if there is a Calling? What if we are WAKING UP? Maybe there was once a tribe of priestesses whose oracles foretold this time of grave danger, and they made a pact. After the Goddess religion fell away, maybe the priestesses slipped into the background, promising to return if they were ever really needed again. What if we are starting to remember magic and each other? Starting to re-member our True selves?

Maybe *we* are the Priestesses, reborn in this time, and we will make the changes needed for our survival. What if it is now our responsibility to change the world? To truly change, we must have a new vision. Really new. A change in worldwide consciousness. And how does one do THAT? Maybe *one* doesn't.

If We are the cells of the Earth, the Goddess, we are being asked to remember ourselves, come together, create true magic and save the planet.

What if it is true, and there is a Calling? Have you heard it? Will you answer? It is time. We can change the world. We are the Priestesses. I hear the Call. Any of you hear it, too?

excerpt © Kim Antieau 2001 with Jeanne Hardy

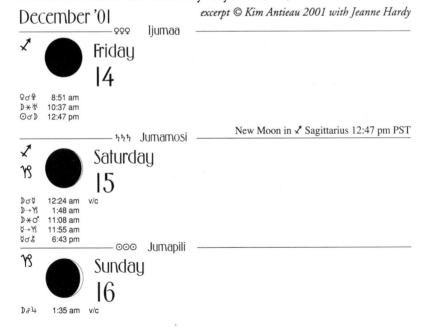

December '01

♀♀♀ Ijumaa

♐

Friday
14

♀♂♀	8:51 am
☽⚹♅	10:37 am
☉♂☽	12:47 pm

New Moon in ♐ Sagittarius 12:47 pm PST

♄♄♄ Jumamosi

♐
♑

Saturday
15

☽♂♉	12:24 am	v/c
☽→♑	1:48 am
☽⚹♂	11:08 am
♉→♑	11:55 am
♉♂♄	6:43 pm

☉☉☉ Jumapili

♑

Sunday
16

☽☍♃	1:35 am	v/c

December
Dezember

🜨
♒

Monday
17

☽→♒ 10:43 am

We are the traveling lightning bolts
Shot from the hand
Of the last woman in our lines
Who knew her power
And threw her flash at the sky

excerpt © Christina Baldwin 2001

ᗧᗧᗧ Dienstag

♒

Tuesday
18

☽☌♆ 12:23 am
☽△♄   6:49 am
☽⚹♀   5:17 pm

☿☿☿ Mittwoch

♒
♓

Wednesday
19

☽⚹♀   5:05 am
☽☌⛢   5:58 am
♀⚹⛢   1:41 pm
☉⚹☽   6:41 pm v/c
☽→♓ 10:09 pm

♃♃♃ Donnerstag

♓

Thursday
20

☽⚹♅   2:28 pm
☽☌♂   3:58 pm
☽□♄   6:30 pm
☽△♃ 10:35 pm

♀♀♀ Freitag

♓

Friday
21

☽ApG   5:02 am
☽□♀   5:46 am
⛢⚹♂   9:47 am
☉→🜨 11:21 am
☿⚻♄   7:23 pm

Solstice

🜨

Sun in Capricorn 11:21 am PST

All aspects in Pacific Standard Time; add 3 hours for EST; add 8 hours for GMT

Lightning Catcher
© *Maya Dobroth 2000*

♓
♈

Saturday
22

☽□♀	12:44 am	v/c
♂□♄	5:35 am	
☽→♈	10:45 am	

☉□☽	12:56 pm
☉♂⚴	3:25 pm
♀⚹♃	10:59 pm

⊙⊙⊙   Sonntag

Waxing Half Moon in ♓ Pisces 12:56 pm PST

♈

Sunday
23

☽⚹♆	1:08 am
☽⚹♄	6:37 am
☽□♃	10:21 am
☽□♅	12:13 pm
☽△♇	6:15 pm

MOON I

December
Kēkēmapa

——— ☽☽☽ Pō'akahi ———

♈
☽ Monday
♉
24

☽⚹♅ 6:51 am
♂△♃ 11:54 am
☽△♀ 7:21 pm v/c
☽→♉ 10:12 pm

——— ♂♂♂ Pō'alua ———

♉
☽ Tuesday
25

☉△☽ 5:36 am
☽□♆ 12:08 pm
☽⚹♃ 8:10 pm
☽⚹♂ 10:30 pm
♀→♑ 11:25 pm

——— ☿☿☿ Pō'akolu ———

♉
☽ Wednesday
26

☽△☿ 6:51 am
☽□♅ 4:22 pm v/c

——— ♃♃♃ Pō'ahā ———

♉
☿ Thursday
27

☽→♊ 6:39 am
♀☌♇ 7:46 am
☽△♆ 7:52 pm
☽♂♄ 11:54 pm

——— ♀♀♀ Pō'alima ———

♊
☽ Friday
28

☽□♂ 8:36 am
☽☍♀ 11:10 am
☽△♅ 10:24 pm v/c

All aspects in Pacific Standard Time; add 3 hours for EST; add 8 hours for GMT

Lori Berenson, Socabaya Prison

Lori Berenson is a human rights activist first sentenced to life imprisonment in Arequipa, Peru as a terrorist by the Fujimori government. She then had her sentence withdrawn by the military tribunal. At press time she is currently being tried by a civil court on charges of co-conspiracy. See Resources, page 188.

"The violation of human rights in Peru isn't only a problem of lack of democracy, freedom of speech and press, and the existence of judicial systems that are completely subordinate to political power. The foremost violation is the institutional violence that relegates the vast majority of people to living in misery. The right to food, health, education and employment are human rights that are consistently violated in Peru; we know that there is spreading hunger and misery and far too many deaths that result from neglect.

In addition, the judicial systems in Peru have sentenced thousands, falsely accused as I was, to live in prisons under horrendous conditions. I have become more convinced than ever that in the presence of social injustice and abuse, silence is almost as harmful as the injustice itself. To be silent is to be an accomplice. We will not be silent, we will not be quiet, until there is justice and respect for human rights in Peru."

words of Lori Berenson, December 1999 ¤ photo and quote submitted by Joanie Levine 2000

ħħħ　Pō'aono

♊
♋

Saturday
29

☽→♋　11:40 am
⚷ApG　3:12 pm
☽☍♀　7:58 pm

⊙⊙⊙　Lāpule

♋

Sunday
30

⊙☍☽　2:40 am
☽♂♃　6:09 am
♂□♀　10:50 am
☽△♂　3:01 pm
⊙⊼ħ　4:31 pm
♃PrG　5:00 pm

Full Moon in ♋ Cancer 2:40 am PST

December/January
Decembro/Januaro))) lundo ────────────

♋
♌
Monday
31

)☌♀ 5:43 am v/c
)→♌ 2:09 pm
☉☍♃ 9:53 pm

──────── ♂♂♂ mardo ────────────

♌
Tuesday
1

January 2002

)☍♆ 2:29 am
)✶♄ 5:29 am
)△♀ 4:40 pm
)PrG 11:09 pm

──────── ☿☿☿ merkredo ────────────

♌
♍
Wednesday
2

)☍♅ 3:16 am v/c
♀⚹♄ 7:17 am
)→♍ 3:34 pm

──────── ♃♃♃ ĵaŭdo ────────────

♍
Thursday
3

♀☍♃ 4:22 am
)□♄ 6:41 am
)✶♃ 8:34 am
)△♀ 9:01 am
☉△) 1:36 pm
☿→♒ 1:38 pm
)□♀ 6:15 pm
)☍♂ 11:30 pm v/c

──────── ♀♀♀ vendredo ────────────

♍
♎
Friday
4

)→♎ 5:23 pm
)△♅ 8:35 pm

─────────────────────────────────────

All aspects in Pacific Standard Time; add 3 hours for EST; add 8 hours for GMT

Kali-Ma, Fierce Goddess of Change
¤ *Frankie Hansbearry 1996*

ħħħ sabato

♎

Saturday
5

☽△♆ 6:14 am
☽△♄ 8:39 am
☽□♃ 10:20 am
☽□♀ 4:11 pm
☉□☽ 7:55 pm
☽⚹♀ 8:54 pm

⊙⊙⊙ dimanĉo

Waning Half Moon in ♎ Libra 7:55 pm PST

♎
♏

Sunday
6

☽△♅ 8:05 am v/c
☽→♏ 8:41 pm

MOON I   41

January

Januari

 ♏

 ))) Jumatatu

Monday
7

♉ □ ♀ 5:52 am
♉ □ ♆ 10:08 am
♉ △ ♃ 1:45 pm

♏

♂♂ơ Jumanne

Tuesday
♉

☽ ⚹ ♀ 1:41 am
☉ ⚹ ☽ 4:29 am
☽ △ ♂ 12:41 pm
☽ □ ♅ 1:03 pm   v/c

♏
♐

☿☿☿ Jumatano

Wednesday
9

☽ → ♐ 1:57 am
☿ ☌ ♆ 3:56 am
☽ ⚹ ♆ 4:05 pm
☽ ⚹ ♉ 5:17 pm
☽ ☍ ♄ 5:59 pm

♐

♃♃♃ Alhamisi

Thursday
10

☿ △ ♄ 12:36 am
☽ ☌ ♀ 7:54 am
☿ ⊼ ♃ 12:19 pm
☽ ⚹ ♅ 8:07 pm
☽ □ ♂ 10:49 pm   v/c

♐
♑

♀♀♀ Ijumaa

Friday
11

☽ → ♑ 9:18 am

New Moon

Late last night Mom and I walked to the crossroads and left an offering for Hecate: a white blossom and three apples cut open to reveal the star/pentagram inside. Under the protecting heaviness of Elms, Mom placed the apples in a circle around the bloom. Our offering looked small and beautiful against the asphalt, under the low yellow light of the street lamp. "For you, Hecate who brings us both death and life." Mom's voice sounded strong and good. We stood a moment in silence then crossed out of the center and walked home. I looked back just once. I am always aware of how these small humble gestures feel oddly dangerous. How two women, mother and daughter, leaving an offering for the Queen of the Dead at this city crossroads would freak some people out.

Such a small, simple gesture means more than it seems. Hecate is not gone, not dead, She beats under the asphalt and little square lawns of my neighborhood. She comes to the crossroads when we have gone, smells the heavy scent of blossoms, the sweetness of apples. She smiles to be remembered, to have survived. We have survived.

¤ *Ellen Marie Hinchcliffe 2000, for my Mother*

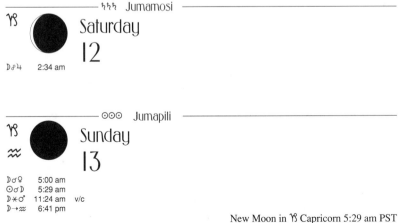

ħħħ Jumamosi

♑

Saturday
12

☽☍♃   2:34 am

☉☉☉ Jumapili

♑
♒

Sunday
13

☽☌♀   5:00 am
☉☌☽   5:29 am
☽☒♂   11:24 am   v/c
☽→♒   6:41 pm

New Moon in ♑ Capricorn 5:29 am PST

The Kapululangu Aboriginal women elders, whose ancestral Country lies in Australia's Great Sandy Desert, asked me to tell you (because they don't write English) that they are working hard to keep their Country strong. These same women walked these desert tracks in their youth before the white invaders forced them out in the late 1940s.

Together we traveled to the Nakarra Nakarra (Seven Sisters) Dreaming place. A sacred women's site. A cluster of hills rising above the flat plain of the spinifex desert. Each hill an ancestor, a relative, a living spirit. This is where these strong independent women performed ceremony during the Dreaming. The breast-shaped hills are peaked by small outcrops of nipple-like red rock. Over and over each is pointed out to me so I will know who is who. They are Napaltjarris, Nakamarras, Napurrulas.

For hours we sit in the sand painting up for ceremony. The elders dip their fingers in a mixture of fat and ochre. Apply it in the age-old designs to breasts, shoulders and upper arms, all the time singing in an earthy drone-like chant. Fingers skim across skin. Red landscape is transferred to black bodies. The songs for this place, transferred from mother to daughter for aeons, invigorate the ceremonial ground. The ceremonial pole is decorated and planted in the dancing circle. The singers take their places, sitting in an arc. The dancers, Manyaya and Tjama, further decorated with feathers and leafy branches, approach from the cover of the nearby scrub. Dancing through Country the familiar Napanangkas are temporarily transformed into mythical beings.

The Nakarra Nakarra defeated the predatory males who pursued them. These elders are likewise preserving their secret and sacred women's spiritual traditions. Looking after their Country and keeping the lore strong, though it is dangerously threatened by predatory White culture.

So we traveled on, to Parrakurra, the site where the Seven Sisters emerged from underground—a powerful women's initiation site too secret to be described here. The elders insist there will never be mining here. They will never allow it. It must remain protected forever. "You tell them Napaltjarri, we want people to respect our Culture," they said to me, and so this is what I am telling you.

◻ *Chris "Napaltjarri" Sitka 2001*

See Resources, page 188.

TOP: *Elders Performing Ceremony at Nakarra Nakarra Women's Site*
BOTTOM LEFT: *Yudiyu Nampitjin*   **BOTTOM RIGHT:** *Nunginurra Napanangka*
© Chris Sitka 2001

January
Januar

───── ☽☽☽   Montag ─────

≈ Monday

14

☉☌♀ 3:32 am
☽☌♇ 10:13 am
☽△♄ 11:27 am
☽☌♂ 8:43 pm

Ixchel

───── ♂♂♂   Dienstag ─────

≈ Tuesday

15

☽⚹♀ 3:09 am
☽☌♅ 4:25 pm   v/c

───── ☿☿☿   Mittwoch ─────

≈
♓ Wednesday

16

♀ApG 12:29 am
☽→♓ 6:00 am
☽□♄ 11:02 pm
☽△♃ 11:09 pm

───── ♃♃♃ Donnerstag ─────

♓ Thursday

17

☽□♀ 3:27 pm

───── ♀♀♀   Freitag ─────

♓
♈ Friday

18

☽ApG 12:46 am
☿sR 12:50 pm
♂→♈ 2:53 pm
☉⚹☽ 4:00 pm
☽⚹♀ 6:27 pm   v/c
☽→♈ 6:35 pm
☽☌♂ 6:49 pm
♀→≈ 7:42 pm

© Lynn Dewart 1999

All aspects in Pacific Standard Time; add 3 hours for EST; add 8 hours for GMT

Year at a Glance for ♒ AQUARIUS (Jan. 19–Feb. 18)

If there are optimum times for you to be that Aquarian agent of change, this is a great year. The Aquarian job is to be a prophet and a visionary, so go for it; take yourself seriously in 2002. Invent, innovate through work and community activism. Well-being and satisfaction come from an almighty capacity for daily discipline, especially during the first half of the year.

If you are an artist, take your art more seriously. This may not be a time of flowing expression, but with discipline, your craftswomanship is significantly enhanced. Dream up new techniques, design new tools. Schedule studio time, don't wait around for the muse to call you.

In matters of love—take your love more seriously. Just as in art, you benefit from innovation and good craftswomanship. If you are not serious, love can elude you. If a relationship is not healthy, this year will amplify its restrictiveness. In the latter half of the year new people enter your life. Make sure you are engaged where you want to be. If you have children, this is a good year to really see them as independent individuals. They may feel burdensome at times. Because their needs are very clear, holding a pragmatic perspective will evoke needed strategies.

Your compassionate side is still working overtime trying to save the lost souls who come into your sight, a tendency which may prevent others from fully realizing their own capabilities. Are you encouraging dependence? Certainly, tithe some of your time to worthy causes. This feeds your spirit, but too much mystical self-loss is hard on your health this year. Remember to eat frequent meals, watch iron levels.

© Gretchen Lawlor 2001

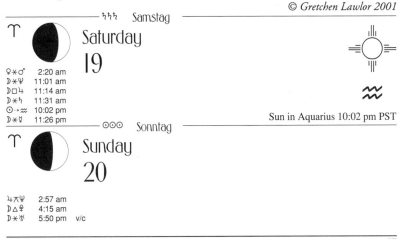

♄♄♄ Samstag

♈ **Saturday**
19

♀⚹♂ 2:20 am
☽⚹♆ 11:01 am
☽☐♃ 11:14 am
☽⚹♄ 11:31 am
☉→♒ 10:02 pm
☽⚹♅ 11:26 pm

Sun in Aquarius 10:02 pm PST

☉☉☉ Sonntag

♈ **Sunday**
20

♃⚹♆ 2:57 am
☽△♀ 4:15 am
☽⚹♅ 5:50 pm v/c

January
'Ianuali

————))) Pō'akahi ————

♈
♉

Monday
21

☽→♉ 6:47 am
☉□☽ 9:46 am
☽□♀ 1:35 pm
☽⚹♃ 10:23 pm
☽□♇ 10:55 pm

□ *Monica Sjöö 2000*

Waxing Half Moon in ♉ Taurus 9:46 am PST

———— ♂♂♂ Pō'alua ————

♉

Tuesday
22

☽□☿ 8:22 am

———— ☿☿☿ Pō'akolu ————

♉
♊

Wednesday
23

♄△♅ 12:16 am
☉⚹♂ 4:25 am
☽□♅ 4:29 am v/c
☽→♊ 4:28 am
☽⚹♂ 11:42 pm

———— ♃♃♃ Pō'ahā ————

♊

Thursday
24

☉△☽ 12:10 am
☽△♀ 4:57 am
☽♂♄ 7:37 am
☽△♅ 7:47 am
☽△♅ 12:52 pm
♀⚹♃ 9:15 pm
☽☍♇ 11:08 pm

———— ♀♀♀ Pō'alima ————

♊
♋

Friday
25

♂□♇ 1:05 am
♀△♄ 8:17 am
♀♂♅ 11:17 am
☽△♅ 11:23 am v/c
☽→♋ 10:17 pm

———————————————————————

All aspects in Pacific Standard Time; add 3 hours for EST; add 8 hours for GMT

At Ephesus

One pillar remains
ancient and rebuilt
abandoned, reclaimed
ragged yet enduring
like my faith.

In this feral place
my prayers become informal
offering belly to sun
toes to pond
breath to breeze, unbound.

Now I blink, turtle eyed, a slow swoon.
Now I soar, swallow breasted, heart lilting.
Now I sink, silty, past clouds of algae
and rise again on the spiral flight
of two red dragonflies, yearning.

One pillar remains
and you are still here
my deep wild
swift wild
sweet wild
Artemis.

When they turned Paul away and vowed
your name would always be praised
they must have known I would be coming.

¤ *Jessica Montgomery 2000*

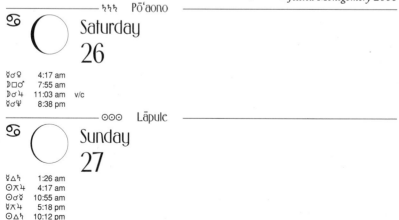

───── ♄♄♄ Pōʻaono ─────

♋

Saturday
26

☿☌♀	4:17 am	
☽□♂	7:55 am	
☽☌♃	11:03 am	v/c
☿☌♆	8:38 pm	

───── ☉☉☉ Lāpule ─────

♋

Sunday
27

☿△♄	1:26 am	
☉☌♃	4:17 am	
☉☌♉	10:55 am	
☿☌♃	5:18 pm	
☉△♄	10:12 pm	

January/February

ⅅⅅⅅ lundo

♋︎
♌︎

Monday
28

☽→♌︎	12:31 am	☽✶♄	1:41 pm
☿✶♂	1:52 am	♂□♃	1:58 pm
☉☌♅	5:45 am	☽☍♆	2:15 pm
☽☍♅	10:54 am	☉☍☽	2:50 pm
☽△♂	12:10 pm	☽☍♀	8:55 pm
♆ApG	1:18 pm		

Full Moon in ♌︎ Leo 2:50 pm PST

♂♂♂ mardo

♌︎

Tuesday
29

☿PrG	12:21 am	
☽△♀	3:50 am	
☽☍♅	3:04 pm	v/c
♂✶♄	6:35 pm	

☿☿☿ merkredo

♌︎
♍︎

Wednesday
30

☽→♍︎	12:40 am
☽PrG	12:55 am
♂✶♆	9:00 am
☽✶♃	11:55 am
☽□♄	1:33 pm

♃♃♃ ĵaŭdo

♍︎

Thursday
31

☽□♀	3:46 am	v/c

♀♀♀ vendredo

♍︎
♎︎

Friday
1

February

☽→♎︎	12:44 am
☽△♅	4:13 am
♀✶♀	8:53 am
☽□♃	11:57 am
☽△♄	1:54 pm
☽△♆	2:49 pm
☽☍♂	5:29 pm
☉△☽	10:24 pm

All aspects in Pacific Standard Time; add 3 hours for EST; add 8 hours for GMT

© *Lena Bartula 2001*

Brigit's Day Invocation

Come join us in celebration
Of the first greening shoots
Proof of the sun's return.

Always with candles and water
We invoke the Holy Bride
On the second day of February
Brigit's Day Triple Moon
Goddess of the Flame
Muse of Poetry
And All the Making Arts
She will come to bless our hearths.

We cast the circle
In the name of Brigit
Goddess of the Flame
Goddess of the Forge
Goddess of Inspiration

With Fire to burn away the old
With air to blow away the old
And water to cleanse the old.
The Virgin renews Herself.

© *Stephanie Griffis 1991*

FROM TOP TO BOTTOM:
Standing Stones, Drombeg, Co. Cork, Ireland □ *Marguerite Bartley 2001*
Kiva in Bandalier Ceremonial Cave, New Mexico □ *Musawa 2000*
Temple of Segesta, Sicily © *Eaglehawk 2001*

Ceridwen

© *Tina Smale 2000*

Priestess Dreams

I dream of Temples—thousands, across the world—sprouting up from Mother Earth like new Spring Buds, providing spaces for womyn to re-awaken, re-member, and re-turn to their Sacred Goddess Selves.

¤ *Phoenix B. Grace 2000*

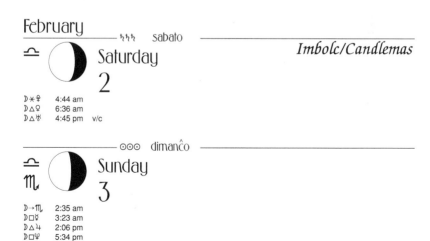

February

♄♄♄ sabato

♎ Saturday
2

Imbolc/Candlemas

☽⚹♀ 4:44 am
☽△♀ 6:36 am
☽△♅ 4:45 pm v/c

☉☉☉ dimanĉo

♎
♏ Sunday
3

☽→♏ 2:35 am
☽□♉ 3:23 am
☽△♃ 2:06 pm
☽□♆ 5:34 pm
♉→♑ 8:17 pm

February

Februari

♏ Monday

4

☉□)	5:33 am
)□♀	3:25 pm
)□♅	9:08 pm

Waning Half Moon in ♏ Scorpio 5:33 am PST

♏
♐ Tuesday

5

)✳♉	6:02 am	v/c
)→♐	7:21 am	
☉✳♀	6:43 pm	
)☌♄	10:01 pm	
)✳♆	11:25 pm	

♐ Wednesday

6

)△♂	8:16 am
)☌♀	2:54 pm
☉✳)	4:35 pm

♐
♑ Thursday

7

)✳♀	4:21 am	
)✳♅	4:38 am	v/c
♀☌♅	7:23 am	
)→♑	3:08 pm	
♄sD	5:32 pm	

♑ Friday

8

)☍♃	3:17 am
♉sD	9:28 am
)□♂	8:43 pm

All aspects in Pacific Standard Time; add 3 hours for EST; add 8 hours for GMT

Touches of Afrika

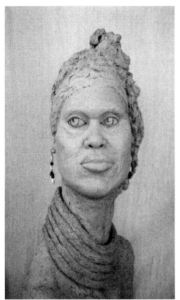

Zwanda Queen of the World
© *Kit Skeoch 2001*

I am a sister lost and found through remembering Afrika. It was so long ago, the memories were not left, but brought along and told to me, and each time, I was renewed with a knowing about who I was and where I had been.

Sisters of the sacred soil, dance to the tune of the drums that syncopate with your heart. Be touched by the priceless spirit. You and I are touched from everywhere we are. We are here and there, you and I see ourselves in each other. I love what I see. It speaks to me and makes me know its presence.

I don't cry for Afrika. It is in me. I am touched by her. She will live through my spirited self. She has spoken to me and requested that I reclaim my light. Move into myself, by being myself. I am of Afrika. A sister of many. Let's move in our circle of togetherness and allow ourselves to be touched.

excerpt © Radhia A. Jaaber 1998

ᕼᕼᕼ Jumamosi

♑ Saturday
9

☽♂♉ 10:50 pm v/c

☉☉☉ Jumapili

♑
♒ Sunday
10

☽→♒ 1:15 am
♃♂♇ 4:58 pm
☽△♄ 5:06 pm
☽♂♆ 6:57 pm

Amma

The divinely beautiful, dark Indian woman lovingly known by millions around the world as Amma, or "Mother," is one of the most extraordinary forces healing our planet today. Born in 1954, in a small poor fishing village on the tropical coast of South India, Amma's first sound was not a cry but a laugh! A brilliant, intensely spiritual child, she had to leave school at age ten to serve her family. Working day and night to feed, clothe and care for the family and livestock, the joyful, energetic little girl continuously poured out her heart to God in prayer, song and dance. Unable to bear to see old women and children go hungry, she gave away food—for which she was severely beaten. Such acts of compassion and devotion increased until finally her family threw her out of the house. Under the coconut palms she lived in ecstasy, talking to Mother Sea, hugging trees, kissing plants, eating only food that animals—cows, dogs, eagles—brought her.

One day a spinning globe of brilliant reddish light appeared and out of it came the glorious form of the Universal Mother wearing a beautiful crown and smiling benevolently. Amma's entire being rushed toward Her in a torrential stream. Her whole body vibrated with the sacred mantra, *Mother, Mother.* In everything, everywhere she saw only Her. She sang, "You are creation, You are creator, You are energy, You are truth, oh Goddess!" At last the Mother, dazzling like a thousand suns, merged into Amma, and told her the purpose of her birth was to comfort suffering humanity.

Since that time, Amma sees in everyone her own Self. She dedicates every moment to loving, helping and serving others. Several times a week, Amma appears in the gorgeous sari-clad form of the Great Goddess, receiving people by the thousands for as long as 20 hours, hugging and blessing each one. Whether illiterate or educated, rich or poor, sick or healthy, worldly or spiritual—each is accepted with the same motherly tenderness. In India, Amma has created for the poor, especially rejected women and children, dozens of schools, colleges, orphanages and hospitals; to 50,000 people, she has given houses, pensions, food and clothing. Around the world, she has built hundreds of spiritual centers and temples. In 20 different languages, books and magazines offer her simple yet profound teaching of *compassionate consciousness*.

Amma's incredible life is a heart-shattering example of true Love, Beauty, Sacrifice, and Supreme Consciousness.

See Resources, page 188.

III. TEACH/GUIDE

Moon III: February 11–March 13

New Moon in ♒ Aquarius: Feb. 11; Sun in ♓ Pisces: Feb. 18; Full Moon in ♍ Virgo: Feb. 27

"Children, go directly to the source of divine Love—
drink to your heart's content from that ocean of Love." *Amma*

February
Februar

――― ☽☽☽　Montag ―――

≈

Monday
11

♂△♀　10:32 am
☽⚹♀　11:23 am
☽⚹♂　11:26 am
♀→♓　5:18 pm
☉☌☽　11:41 pm

Lunar Imbolc
New Moon in ≈ Aquarius 11:41 pm PST

――― ♂♂♂　Dienstag ―――

≈
♓

Tuesday
12

☽☌♅　2:21 am　v/c
☽→♓　12:53 pm
☽☌♀　3:10 pm

――― ☿☿☿　Mittwoch ―――

♓

Wednesday
13

☽△♃　1:03 am
☽□♄　5:05 am
☉☌♅　9:06 am
☿→≈　9:21 am
☽□♀　11:43 pm　v/c

――― ♃♃♃　Donnerstag ―――

♓

Thursday
14

♅ApG　7:35 am
☽ApG　2:20 pm

――― ♀♀♀　Freitag ―――

♓
♈

Friday
15

☽→♈　1:26 am
☽⚹♉　3:31 am
☽□♃　1:27 pm
☽⚹♄　5:49 pm
☽⚹♆　7:58 pm

―――――――――――――――――――――――――――――

All aspects in Pacific Standard Time; add 3 hours for EST; add 8 hours for GMT

Outlaw Teachers

Since 1996, the Taliban, a fundamentalist Islamic militia, has seized control of most of Afghanistan, and imposed a state of gender apartheid which denies basic human rights to women and girls. See Resources, page 188.

Outlaws: those who dare teach young girls
to read, to write
school is outlawed for girls
work is outlawed for women
women are walled up in their homes, windows painted black
walled up behind law from Islamic patriarchy gone mad.

And yet, defiant women quietly teach
defiant families quietly bring their daughters
guerrilla education
a clandestine network of warrior teachers
priestessing a generation.

© *Bethroot Gwynn 2000*

"We are very, very careful. Teachers don't allow any strangers in their school. They only take children from their community—it's like an extended family situation . . . If they are not careful, the teacher can be threatened, her house can be taken away from her, or she can be separated from her family, or the children can be separated from their family . . . These teachers are experienced teachers. They strongly believe in education. That's the reason they put themselves in such a risk and their families in such a risk, by opening these schools . . . I have to be very careful. If my life is being tracked, it's ok. That's my mission. It's risky for me, but I am willing to take that risk."

excerpt ¤ anonymous Afghani woman, the director of thirty-five home-schools for girls in Afghanistan, 2000 (radio interview)

--------- ♮♮♮ Samstag ---------

♈ ● **Saturday**

16

♀△♃	10:18 am	
☽△♀	12:31 pm	
☽♂♂	8:08 pm	

--------- ☉☉☉ Sonntag ---------

♈
♉ ● **Sunday**

17

♀⚹♄	1:53 am	
☽⚹♅	4:01 am	
☉⚹☽	11:55 am	v/c
☽→♉	1:58 pm	
☽□♅	8:01 pm	

February
Pēpēluali

──── ⟩⟩⟩ Pōʻakahi ────────────────

♉
Monday
18

☽✶♃	1:36 am
♀□♄	5:14 am
☽✶♀	6:17 am
☽□♆	8:23 am
☉→♓	12:13 pm

♓

Sun in Pisces 12:13 pm PST

──── ♂♂♂ Pōʻalua ────────────────

♉
Tuesday
19

☽□♅	3:34 pm	v/c

──── ☿☿☿ Pōʻakolu ────────────────

♉
♊
Wednesday
20

☽→♊	12:50 am
☉□☽	4:02 am
☽△♅	11:06 am
☽♂♄	4:22 pm
☽△♆	6:31 pm
☿⊼♃	7:33 pm
☽□♀	10:38 pm

Waxing Half Moon in ♊ Gemini 4:02 am PST

──── ♃♃♃ Pōʻahā ────────────────

♊
Thursday
21

☽☍♇	9:32 am	
☽✶♂	10:55 pm	
☽△♅	11:53 pm	v/c

──── ♀♀♀ Pōʻalima ────────────────

♊
♋
Friday
22

☽→♋	8:16 am
☉△☽	3:39 pm
☽♂♃	6:19 pm
♂✶♅	6:28 pm

───────────────────────────────

All aspects in Pacific Standard Time; add 3 hours for EST; add 8 hours for GMT

Year at a Glance for ♓ PISCES (Feb. 18–March 20)

In 2002, you continue the alchemical process of establishing yourself as outstanding in a way that will be recognized by others. You really want to be somebody this year. Some Pisceans may leave a job due to power struggles or resistance from the status quo. Others will continue to distill down the potent essence of existing work, contacting an inner sense of authority and finding a true giftedness. Your intuition is very active, perhaps in dreams or art, or in instinctive hunches. You are a conduit for information welling out of the collective mind. If you have psychic gifts, expect contact with the more subtle realms of reality; transcendental mystical experiences are possible.

People and situations from your past spring unannounced back into your life. You would do well to cleanse your subconscious of limiting ghosts from your past; you may have little choice as they may literally appear on your doorstep. Take advantage of this time for resolution (2001–2002) to free yourself from ancient guilt, anger or resentment. This prepares you for an important life change in 2003; you are already sensing the rumblings. Now is a good time to establish new emotional supports, foundations upon which you will depend for years to come. Be willing to surrender old security blankets.

You feel more self-assured in love, with children and in your creativity. If not already involved, a love could appear this year. A love in progress could get richer and more inspiring. You may become the mouth-piece of a group which holds your creative values most dear, and manage to do so in a most playful, exuberant manner.   © *Gretchen Lawlor 2001*

Ask, Believe, Receive
© *Lisa de St. Criox 1996*

♄♄♄   Pōʻaono

♋ 🌓 **Saturday**
23

☿△♄   5:52 am
☽△♀   9:47 am

☉☉☉   Lāpule

♋ 🌓 **Sunday**
♌ **24**

☉△♃   3:16 am
☽□♂   5:39 am   v/c
☿☌♆   7:59 am
☽→♌   11:36 am

February/March

Februaro/Marto

☽☽☽ lundo

♌

Monday 25

☽⚹♄ 1:12 am
☽☍♆ 3:06 am
☽☍☿ 4:39 am
☽△♇ 3:57 pm
♀□♇ 4:44 pm
☉⚹⚷ 7:28 pm

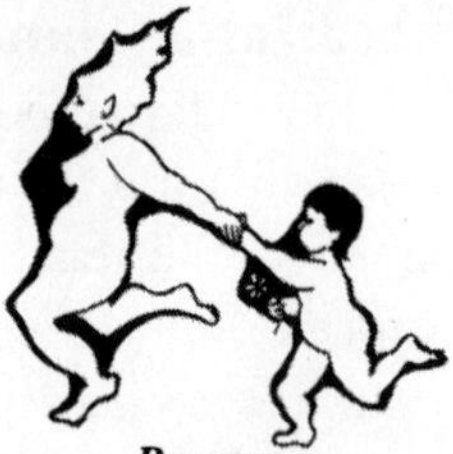

Rescue
© Sequoia Megary Sigler 2000

♂♂♂ mardo

♌ ♍

Tuesday 26

☽☍♅ 4:47 am
☽△♂ 8:30 am v/c
☽→♍ 11:47 am
☉□♄ 7:54 pm
☽⚹♃ 8:38 pm

☿☿☿ merkredo

♍

Wednesday 27

☽□♄ 12:56 am
☉☍☽ 1:17 am
☽PrG 11:54 am
☽□♇ 3:12 pm
☽☍♀ 7:17 pm v/c

Full Moon in ♍ Virgo 1:17 am PST

♃♃♃ ĵaŭdo

♍ ♎

Thursday 28

☽→♎ 10:47 am
☽□♃ 7:39 pm

♀♀♀ vendredo

♎

Friday 1

March

☽△♄ 12:08 am
☽△♆ 1:59 am
♂→♉ 7:05 am
♃sD 7:14 am
☽△☿ 11:40 am
☽⚹♇ 2:36 pm

All aspects in Pacific Standard Time; add 3 hours for EST; add 8 hours for GMT

Great Aunt Minnie
Grandmother, piano player for the silent pictures, card reader and sage.

© *Diane Bergstrom 2001*

 sabato

♎︎
♏︎ ☽ Saturday
2

☽△♅ 3:57 am v/c
☽→♏︎ 10:51 am
☽☍♂ 12:16 pm
☽△♃ 8:10 pm
☿⚹♀ 9:39 pm

⊙⊙⊙ dimanĉo

♏︎ ☽ Sunday
3

☽□♆ 2:57 am
⊙△☽ 8:23 am
☽□♅ 6:13 pm

March

Machi

―――― ☽☽☽　Jumatatu ――――――――――――――――――

Monday
4

☽△♀　6:19 am
☽□♅　6:43 am　v/c
☽→♐　1:55 pm

―――― ♂♂♂　Jumanne ――――――――――――――――――

Tuesday
5

☽☍♄　5:19 am
☽⚹♆　7:21 am
☉□☽　5:24 pm
☽☌♀　9:36 pm

Waning Half Moon in ♐ Sagittarius 5:24 pm PST

―――― ☿☿☿　Jumatano ――――――――――――――――――

Wednesday
6

☽⚹♅　6:00 am
☽⚹♅　1:19 pm
☽□♀　6:31 pm　v/c
☽→♑　8:48 pm

―――― ♃♃♃　Alhamisi ――――――――――――――――――

Thursday
7

☽△♂　4:43 am
☽☍♃　7:36 am
♀→♈　5:42 pm

―――― ♀♀♀　Ijumaa ――――――――――――――――――

Friday
8

☉□♀　12:27 am
☉⚹☽　7:06 am　v/c

Those People

"Any questions?" The subject was a one-act play but questions came from whatever else was on their minds.

"Why do you teach THOSE people?" A student who pressed herself against the back wall raised her hand. "It just bothers me that you teach THOSE people."

"Here's why," I said. "Once I saw a policeman tell a woman to put her hands behind her back so he could cuff her. She had a raincoat and a paperback book and I saw that she was baffled as to what to do with her load while being handcuffed. Just then it occurred to me that many people would not be in trouble if they were accustomed to kindness and common human dignity. Even though the officer shot me a look that said 'you could be next,' I held the coat and book while he cuffed her, then I tucked her things under her arms. She looked surprised, like nobody had ever offered her help before. Should anyone be surprised by kindness?

"Now I teach creative writing in a women's prison, to those people. It's better to get their feelings on paper than to have them beat their heads bloody on the cement wall. Most of the women in maximum security are non-violent. No matter what you hear, no maximum security prison has gained country club status. Do we want them to come out believing the world is cold and cruel, or do we want them to come out knowing they have a chance, knowing someone cares?"

"Thank you," said the student. "I believe you answered my question."

¤ *Linda "Bucky" Marshall 2001*

───── ♄♄♄ Jumamosi ─────

♑
≈≈

Saturday
9

♉☌♅ 1:52 am
☽→≈ 6:56 am
♂⚹♃ 9:46 am
☽⚹♀ 11:12 am
☽□♂ 6:50 pm

───── ☉⊙☉ Jumapili ─────

≈≈

Sunday
10

☽△♄ 12:34 am
☽☌♆ 2:38 am
☽⚹♀ 6:01 pm

Acteal, Chiapas, Mexico 1997

The morning of December 22 found the people of Acteal praying for peace in their church on the edge of the mountain. As suddenly as the wind shifted, a local government-supported paramilitary group attacked, killing forty-five men women and children. All over the Zona Norte this violence swept its cold hand throughout the indigenous communities, taking people from their homes, burning crops and leaving families no choice but to become refugees in their own land.

In spite of the walls of men with machine guns, in spite of the tanks, the trucks, and the helicopters . . . the people of Acteal returned to their community one week later. Walking nine miles from the refugee camp in Polho to the grave that had been dug for their mothers, fathers, brothers, sisters, daughters, sons, friends and lovers, carrying bricks made of red earth and long white candles, they marched past the military encampments to the embankment where their loved ones had fallen. Red earth for the blood that was shed, white candles for the spirit that persists: with these elements we built a monument for the dead and lit candles for peace that burned long into the night.

Mothers, daughters and sisters kept the fires burning throughout this pouring reign of terror, drove back the encroaching soldiers with sticks, fists and stones, made 10 tortillas seem like 100. These women rooted their feet into the soft earth and refused to let their children be shadowed by Fear, refused to let their sacred space be further desecrated by the heavy hand of globalization.

See Resources, page 188.   *photos and writing ¤ Sara Joy Fishkin 2001*

IV. RENEW/REBUILD

Moon IV: March 13–April 12

New Moon in ♓ Pisces: March 13; Sun in ♈ Aries: March 20;
Full Moon in ♎ Libra: March 28

These pictures reflect the magic and power of the women who survived the Acteal massacre. Through their everyday efforts to assert themselves in the face of large scale military intimidation, they are priestessing the planet—restoring life where there has been death and injustice, reaffirming the bonds of family and community and emanating a resiliency of spirit that can never be extinguished.

March
März

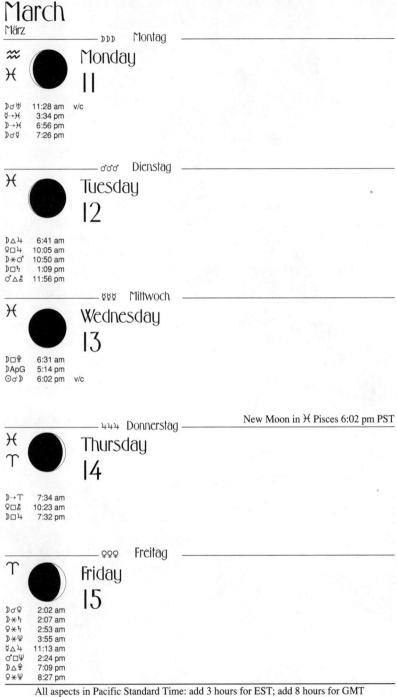

──── ⅅⅅⅅ Montag ────

♒︎
♓︎   Monday
             11

☾☌♅ 11:28 am v/c
☿→♓︎ 3:34 pm
☾→♓︎ 6:56 pm
☾☌♇ 7:26 pm

──── ♂︎♂︎♂︎ Dienstag ────

♓︎   Tuesday
             12

☾△♃ 6:41 am
♀□♃ 10:05 am
☾✶♂︎ 10:50 am
☾□♄ 1:09 pm
♂︎△⚷ 11:56 pm

──── ☿☿☿ Mittwoch ────

♓︎   Wednesday
             13

☾□♀ 6:31 am
☾ApG 5:14 pm
☉☌☾ 6:02 pm v/c

──── ♃♃♃ Donnerstag ────   New Moon in ♓︎ Pisces 6:02 pm PST

♓︎
♈︎   Thursday
             14

☾→♈︎ 7:34 am
♀□⚷ 10:23 am
☾□♃ 7:32 pm

──── ♀♀♀ Freitag ────

♈︎   Friday
             15

☾☌♀ 2:02 am
☾✶♄ 2:07 am
♀✶♄ 2:53 am
☾✶♆ 3:55 am
☿△♃ 11:13 am
♂︎□♆ 2:24 pm
☾△♀ 7:09 pm
♀✶♆ 8:27 pm

All aspects in Pacific Standard Time: add 3 hours for EST; add 8 hours for GMT

Move the River
¤ *Angela Baker 1996*

ᚻᚻᚻ ── Samstag ──────────────

♈ **Saturday**
♉ **16**

☽⚹♅ 1:07 pm v/c
☽→♉ 8:01 pm

──────── ☉☉☉ ── Sonntag ──────────────

♉ **Sunday**
17

☿⚹♃ 12:22 am
☽⚹♃ 8:06 am
☿□♄ 1:29 pm
☽⚹♂ 2:51 pm
☽□♆ 4:15 pm
☽♂♂ 7:12 pm

Priestessing the Planet

I used to bury the corpses of birds hit by cars
hearing their sweet song sisters straining
I thought it gave back to the earth, the Mother who embraces
even sparrows after they fall.
I picked up the garbage left by other people
and separated my plastics from my glass from my metal.
I held the injured wild things, kept in shoeboxes
and released the ones who made it through
and cried over those that did not.
I used cloth diapers, drying them on winter lines
till they were stiff as flags, a symbol of my determination
not to be a landfill mother.
At take-out places,
I refused the styrofoam making them rewrap it
in waxed paper
and I carried my own coffee cup and paid the extra
when they snivelled at the size.
I walked when it was too short to bike
and biked when it was too short to drive
and caught rides in loaded cars when ever else.
It would seem like much, all I have done
but I want to leave the world, ashes scattered to the wind
knowing that I have tried, dear mother, I have tried
and after all, all you ever expected was us to try our best
as only a mother can.

© *Mara Friedman 2000*

Spring Equinox

Spring Equinox is a time when the day and night force are equal, when plants begin to burst forth from the earth, when leaves appear on the trees, and the movement of insects is felt again. Spring is the time when Persephone returns from the underworld as a young girl; mother and daughter play together out in the fields and usher in the new growth. It is a time for each of us to honor the child within and give voice to that child. It is also a time to cleanse our bodies and spirits in preparation for the rebirth.

The celebration of Easter occurs close to the time of this Equinox. *Oestre* or *Eostar* was a feast of the Goddess Ishtar/Astarte/Esther and celebrated her rebirth. The egg was used as a symbol for Eostar as it represented the birth of the Goddess and of all nature.

Prior to the Equinox, it is important that each woman do some individual cleansing. Letting go of old material in the body precipitates the letting go of old emotions stored up in the dark of winter. The night before Equinox, or that day, it is good to do a special sweat.

© *Marcia Starck 1993, reprinted from* We'Moon '95, *excerpted from* Women's Medicine Ways: Cross-Cultural Rites of Passage (*Crossing Press*)

March
Malaki

♉

Monday
18

♉
♊

Tuesday
19

☽□♅ 12:53 am
☉✻☽ 4:53 am   v/c
☽→♊ 7:20 am
☿✻♂ 6:12 pm

♊

Wednesday
20

☽♂♄ 1:40 am
☽△♆ 3:00 am
♀sR 6:53 am
☽□♉ 10:29 am
☉→♈ 11:16 am
☽✻♀ 1:56 pm
☽☍♀ 5:05 pm

Equinox

♈

Sun in Aries 11:16 am PST

♊
♋

Thursday
21

☽△♅ 10:14 am   v/c
☽→♋ 4:06 pm
☉□☽ 6:28 pm
♀△♀ 10:20 pm

Waxing Half Moon in ♋ Cancer 6:28 pm PST

♋

Friday
22

☽♂♃ 3:37 am
☿□♀ 11:10 am
☽✻♂ 7:21 pm

Chant for Planting with Kids

Precious seeds
that we do sow
It's time to sprout,
time to grow!
Up goes your stem,
down goes your root
We'll tend you well—
please bear us fruit!

 ¤ *Elena Margo 2001*

Year at a Glance for ♈ ARIES (March 20–April 19)

In 2002, there is a wellspring of self-confidence you could tap into. With a determination to discipline your mind and focus your interests, now would be a good time to study, to become an authority on something. Doing this now will improve prospects for your future. Right now you are feeling more patient than is normal—for Aries anyway. You are discovering a capacity to express your ideas in an orderly fashion while still holding on to the originality of your thinking.

Recently you may have met some like-minded souls who share some progressive stance with you. It is a good time to align your efforts with others for common gain. If there is a spiritual component to the connection, so much the better. Remember Aries—your gift to the rest of us is your infectious enthusiasm and foolhardy boldness. Lead us on! In the second half of the year bring art, music, prayer into your gatherings. It is a good time to take chances–your destiny could shift in a moment.

A sibling (or close acquaintance) may be demanding; take it as an opportunity to clear up some old business. You could be stuck in a communication rut. Be willing to radically alter your own attitude. You feel more generous towards the world in general, especially October onwards. Day to day responsibilities may drag you down. If you really feel stuck, take time out. A trip or a workshop could help you prioritize and transform your perspective. Some Aries will relocate in the next few years because of a visit to someplace that feels upbeat and promising in 2002.

© *Gretchen Lawlor 2001*

Nelle
© *Sharon Hart 2000*

♄♄♄   Pōʻaono

♋
♌
Saturday
23

☽△♅   1:38 am
☽□♀   2:19 am   v/c
☽→♌   9:12 pm

☉☉☉   Lāpule

♌
Sunday
24

☉△☽   3:24 am
☽⚹♄   1:48 pm
☽☌♆   2:37 pm

March
Marto

♌
♍   ## Monday
25

☽□♂	1:06 am
☽△♃	2:40 am
☽△♀	9:41 am
☽☌♅	5:57 pm v/c
☽→♍	10:43 pm

© Lynda R. Healy 2001

Raven's Moon

♍   ## Tuesday
26

☽⚹♃	9:18 am
♂⚻♀	9:47 am
☽□♄	2:39 pm

♍
♎ ## Wednesday
27

☽□♀	2:39 am
☽△♂	3:28 am
☉□♃	5:24 am
☽☌♅	5:31 pm v/c
☽→♎	10:04 pm
☽PrG	11:35 pm

♎ ## Thursday
28

☽□♃	8:41 am
☉☌☽	10:25 am
☽△♄	1:58 pm
☽△♆	2:23 pm

Full Moon in ♎ Libra 10:04 pm PST

♎
♏ ## Friday
29

☽⚹♀	1:41 am
♅→♈	6:44 am
☉□♇	10:43 am
♀⚹♅	4:24 pm
☽△♅	4:54 pm
☽☌♀	4:57 pm v/c
☽→♏	9:21 pm

All aspects in Pacific Standard Time: add 3 hours for EST; add 8 hours for GMT

The Bloodsisters Project
When the Private Becomes Public

Bloodsisters is an exciting launching pad girl-base that fuels action to combat the silence surrounding our female bodies. We are girls using our own feminine protection to work against the corporate and cultural constructions of menstruation. We are concerned with the serious health, environmental and psychological ramifications of the toxic feminine hygiene industry and are fighting to stop the whitewash on all fronts. Born out of a guerilla girl recyclable-pad distribution network, we are an ever-growing group generating creative projects to raise awareness surrounding menstrual girl-body politics.

Toxic chemicals are contained in disposable products that are bleached with chlorine compounds. There is accumulating evidence that industrial uses of chlorine, including pulp and paper bleaching, release toxic dioxins which bioaccumulate in the environment causing serious harm to wildlife. Dioxin, a by-product of the chlorine bleaching process, is used in tampons and has serious health impacts including endometriosis, cervical cancer, toxic shock syndrome, headaches and so on. Additionally, tampons and disposable pads are often over packaged and cause enormous waste. The average woman will go through about 10,000 pads or tampons in her life.

◻ *Bloodsisters Project 2001*

See Resources, page 188.

--------- ♄♄♄　　sabato ---------

♏ ☽ **Saturday**
        30

☽△♃	8:34 am
☽□♆	2:16 pm
☉✳♄	10:22 pm

--------- ⊙⊙⊙　　dimancô ---------

♏ ☽ **Sunday**
♐   **31**

☉✳♆	1:19 am	
☽☍♂	7:39 am	
☽□♅	6:13 pm	v/c
♀→♉	10:39 pm	
☽→♐	10:48 pm	

April
Aprili

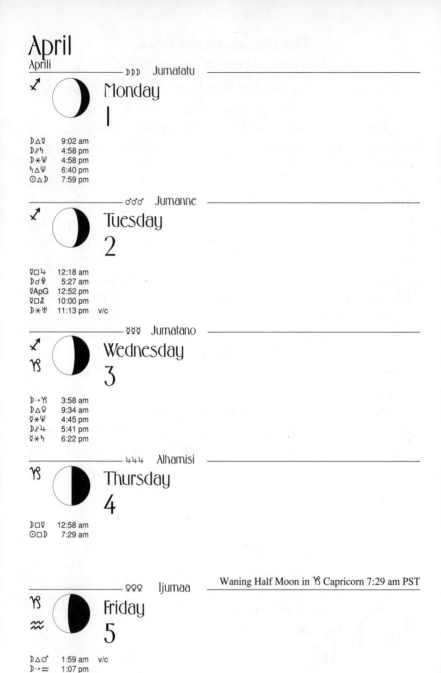

─────))) Jumatatu ─────────────────────────

♐

Monday
1

☽△☿	9:02 am
☽⚹♄	4:58 pm
☽⚹♆	4:58 pm
♄△♆	6:40 pm
☉△☽	7:59 pm

───── ♂♂♂ Jumanne ─────────────────────────

♐

Tuesday
2

☿□♃	12:18 am
☽♂♀	5:27 am
☿ApG	12:52 pm
☿□⚷	10:00 pm
☽⚹♅	11:13 pm v/c

───── ☿☿☿ Jumatano ─────────────────────────

♐
♑

Wednesday
3

☽→♑	3:58 am
☽△♀	9:34 am
☿⚹♆	4:45 pm
☽⚹♃	5:41 pm
☿⚹♄	6:22 pm

───── ♃♃♃ Alhamisi ─────────────────────────

♑

Thursday
4

☽□☿	12:58 am
☉□☽	7:29 am

───── ♀♀♀ Ijumaa ───── Waning Half Moon in ♑ Capricorn 7:29 am PST

♑
♒

Friday
5

☽△♂	1:59 am v/c
☽→♒	1:07 pm

───

All aspects in Pacific Standard Time: add 3 hours for EST; add 8 hours for GMT

Carole Crews, Earth Plaster Teacher

¤ *Marna 1996*

House Frosting/Earthen Plastering

Cob earthen walls are big batches of sand, dirt and straw mixed and slow-baked by the sun. Naturally built walls aren't painted, they're frosted—with earthen plasters that include things like cooked wheat flour paste, eggs, seed powders, a little oil, pure water and milk, along with finer clays, sifted sand, and fiber such as hair or grated straw. Hand mixed and hand applied, these finishes endure.

¤ *Marna 2001*

ʔʔʔ Jumamosi

≈

Saturday
6

☽□♀	1:32 am
☽☌♆	10:04 am
☽△♄	10:43 am
☽⚹♅	11:15 pm
☉⚹☽	11:25 pm
☽⚹♀	11:54 pm

☉☉☉ Jumapili

≈

Sunday
7

☉☌♅	12:55 am	
☿△♀	3:59 am	
☉△♀	6:14 am	
♀⚹♃	6:38 am	
☽□♂	6:06 pm	
☽☌♅	9:01 pm	v/c

Daylight Savings Time begins 2:00 am PST

April
April

──────))) Montag ──────

≈
♓

Monday
8

☽→♓	1:57 am
♀△♇	8:53 am
☽△♃	5:57 pm
☽⚹♀	9:40 pm

────── ♂♂♂ Dienstag ──────

♓

Tuesday
9

☽□♄	12:35 am
☽□♀	1:24 pm
♀□♆	3:51 pm
☽ApG	10:30 pm

────── ☿☿☿ Mittwoch ──────

♓
♈

Wednesday
10

♂□♅	2:04 am	
☽⚹♂	10:31 am	v/c
☽→♈	2:40 pm	

────── ♃♃♃ Donnerstag ──────

♈

Thursday
11

☽□♃	7:14 am
☽⚹♆	12:17 pm
☽⚹♄	1:44 pm

────── ♀♀♀ Freitag ──────

♈

Friday
12

☿⚹♅	1:46 am
☽△♀	1:54 am
☉☌☽	12:21 pm
☽⚹♅	10:34 pm

New Moon in ♈ Aries 12:21 pm PST

All aspects in Pacific Daylight Time; add 3 hours for EDT; add 7 hours for GMT

revolution: to make again a garden of this place

on the hands of the complicit, culpability is bright scarlet
and my conviction is only fortified.

the days of the prison industrial complex are marked.
the world trade organization and the world bank
and the monsantos and the disneys and the duponts
are going the way of dinosaurs

we, justice loving feminists, anarchists, anti-imperialists,
we, Sojourner Truth's children, the children of Emma Goldman,
Rosa Luxemberg, Ida B. Wells and Ella Baker
we, the green, the freedom claiming and self-determining
are undoing your murderous mania.

we are taking back the power to *see* another way.
we are throwing light on your horrorshow,
exposing you in back rooms, boardrooms and conventions
to air your secrets, lies and unaccountable violence.

we're sitting down in the streets, waltzing into your offices,
smashing your missiles and blood soaked coffee empires
disrupting your dirty business as usual
in traffic, on bridges, in the courts, on your bases
building unity and new models,
arming ourselves with economics theory and compassion
we're bent on being human, and don't have another minute
for your hate, for your greed, for your repression
we are taking the world
of white supremacist capitalist patriarchy
carefully and absolutely apart.

◻ *Elizabeth Roberts 2000*

———— ♄♄♄ Samstag ————

♈
♉

Saturday
13

☽♂♅	2:52 am	v/c
☽→♉	2:55 am	
☿→♉	3:10 am	
♂→♊	10:36 am	
☽⚹♃	7:49 pm	

———— ☉☉☉ Sonntag ————

♉

Sunday
14

☽□♆	12:14 am
☽♂♀	11:46 am

*Reclaiming
the Sacred Source:
Claire*
□ *Lynn Creighton 1996*

Women's Sacred Erotic Work: Reclaiming the Body

The foundation of sacred erotic work is a deep acceptance of the whole self, an acceptance of the much ignored and maligned body. As women, who have been taught repression and hatred of our bodily functions and desires, this acceptance is a pioneering first step towards claiming and honoring our bodies as the sacred vessels of our spirits. Sacred erotic work is significantly different than other spiritual practices that deny or ignore the body. It is a path that embraces and explores the body's ecstatic energy as a gateway to truth and inner peace. It does not deny the wisdom and beauty of the mind, but instead embraces awareness as a means of perceiving and working with the energy and impulses of the body. The ecstatic path engages the entire being from the root, or sex, up through the belly, the heart, the mind and beyond, allowing us to fully open to ourselves and the universe.

When we sit together, the stories start to come out: stories of being slapped or shamed when we started bleeding, stories of being called a slut, stories from women whose partners have never looked at, touched, or appreciated their sexual parts, stories from brave women who have never taken a look "down there" and who are starting a positive relationship with their genitals for the first time.

We learn to experience our bodies from the inside out again, from a place of sensation rather than how we look in the mirror or what others might think. The process of welcoming these bodily events, the creation of a sacred circle, a sanctuary for the natural expressions of the body, is profoundly healing.

excerpt □ *Ruby Juices 1998*

*Reclaiming
the Sacred Source:
Dandelion*
◻ *Lynn Creighton 1996*

April
'Apelila

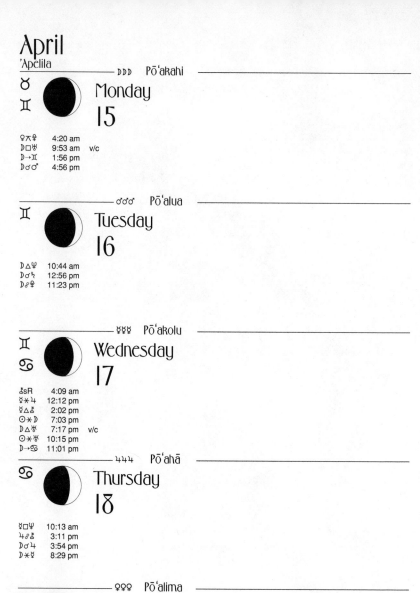

━━━ ⃰DDD Pōʻakahi ━━━━━━━━━━━━

♉
♊
Monday
15

♀⊼♇ 4:20 am
D□♅ 9:53 am   v/c
D→♊ 1:56 pm
D♂♂ 4:56 pm

━━━ ♂♂♂ Pōʻalua ━━━━━━━━━━━━

♊
Tuesday
16

D△♆ 10:44 am
D♂♄ 12:56 pm
D☍♀ 11:23 pm

━━━ ☿☿☿ Pōʻakolu ━━━━━━━━━━━━

♊
♋
Wednesday
17

♃sR 4:09 am
☿✶♃ 12:12 pm
☿△♄ 2:02 pm
☉✶D 7:03 pm
D△♅ 7:17 pm   v/c
☉✶♅ 10:15 pm
D→♋ 11:01 pm

━━━ ♃♃♃ Pōʻahā ━━━━━━━━━━━━

♋
Thursday
18

♀□♆ 10:13 am
♃☍♄ 3:11 pm
D♂♃ 3:54 pm
D✶♀ 8:29 pm

━━━ ♀♀♀ Pōʻalima ━━━━━━━━━━━━

♋
Friday
19

D✶♀ 4:55 pm   v/c
☉→♉ 11:20 pm

♉

Sun in Taurus 11:20 pm PDT

All aspects in Pacific Daylight Time; add 3 hours for EDT; add 7 hours for GMT

Year at a Glance for ♉ TAURUS (April 19–May 20)

In 2002 Taurus may experience an accentuated craving for learning, teaching and travel, continuing a developmental cycle seeded in May 2000. Your attitude is upbeat, tolerant and generous. Inspiration and downright lucky opportunities abound close at hand through friends, siblings or neighbors. From July onwards improvements in your domestic situation reflect an improved relationship with your inner self. Your base of operations benefits from expansion. Some Taureans may need to move. Others benefit from adding personal space to an existing dwelling.

Professionally there is a lot going on. You are just full of inspirations, innovations and rebellious quirkiness. Job changes have become commonplace for you in the last six years. There is a chance you will finally find or create the job that matches your determinedly individualistic self. Check with a practical friend or even a career professional before making a huge investment in the dream job. Dealing with financial constraints this year brings out the best of your resourceress self and sets you off on a productive reappraisal and deepening of your values. Your material status could change significantly due to outside influences.

You may have experienced a significant loss in the past few years. Residual melancholia lightens with sharing the burden with others, and everyone stands to benefit from the exchange. Consider writing about it. You may find yourself recycling emotional issues of your early years, reactivated by this loss or by seemingly unrelated difficult interactions with intimates. This is a good time for an emotional housecleaning, especially in the latter half of the year. Then, you are able to break through defensive attitudes that have kept you from deeper contact with intimates.

© *Gretchen Lawlor 2001*

Unveiled
© *Carol Wylie 2000*

Waxing Half Moon in ♌ Leo 5:48 am PDT

----------- ♄♄♄　Pōʻaono -----------

♋
♌

Saturday
20

☽→♌	5:20 am
☉□☽	5:48 am
☽✶♂	1:51 pm

----------- ☉☉☉　Lāpule -----------

♌

Sunday
21

☽☌♅	12:13 am
☽✶♄	2:56 am
☽□♉	9:54 am
☽△♀	11:20 am
☿⊼♀	8:56 pm

April
Aprilo

© *Loretta Joseph 2000*

Earth Angel

ⅅⅅⅅ   lundo

♌︎
♍︎

Monday
22

☽□♀	1:42 am	
☽☍♅	5:30 am	v/c
☽→♍︎	8:35 am	
☉△☽	12:43 pm	
☽□♂	7:05 pm	

♂♂♂   mardo

♍︎

Tuesday
23

☽⚹♃	12:39 am
☽□♄	5:23 am
☽□♀	12:57 pm
☽△☿	6:23 pm
♀□♅	11:32 pm

☿☿☿   merkredo

♍︎
♎︎

Wednesday
24

☽△♀	7:06 am	v/c
☽→♎︎	9:22 am	
☽△♂	9:49 pm	

♃♃♃   ĵaŭdo

♎︎

Thursday
25

☽□♃	1:25 am
☽△♆	2:45 am
☽△♄	5:55 am
☽PrG	9:29 am
♀→♊︎	10:57 am
☽⚹♀	12:56 pm

♀♀♀   vendredo

♎︎
♏︎

Friday
26

☽△♅	6:29 am	v/c
☽→♏︎	9:15 am	
♂⛎♇	7:23 pm	
☉☍☽	8:00 pm	

Lunar Beltane
Full Moon in ♏︎ Scorpio 8:00 pm PDT

All aspects in Pacific Daylight Time; add 3 hours for EDT; add 7 hours for GMT

Tincture Making

digging roots
of echinacea and valerian

to strengthen my resistance
to quiet my restless sleep

exposing the source
of innocent flowers

dirty secrets
and childhood traumas

washing the wounds
with the sting of vodka

made into medicine
with the patience of time

¤ *Colleen Redman 2001*

Echinacea
© *Amy Schutzer 1994*

ħħħ   sabato

♏   Saturday
27

☽△♃   1:56 am
☽□♆   2:50 am

☉☉☉   dimanĉo

♏   Sunday
♐   **28**

☽☌♉   6:19 am
☽□♅   7:25 am   v/c
☽→♐   10:13 am
☽☌♀   4:50 pm
☿□♅   6:03 pm

April/May
Aprili/Mei

♐

Monday
29

☽☌♂	4:15 am
☽⚹♆	4:41 am
☉△⚷	6:04 am
☽⚹♄	8:50 am
♂△♆	1:27 pm

Lune
□ *Melissa McConnell 2000*

♐
♑

Tuesday
30

☽☌♀	3:30 pm	
☿→♊	12:15 am	
☽⚹♅	11:10 am	v/c
☽→♑	2:03 pm	
♃⚼♆	6:45 pm	

♑

Wednesday
1

☉□♆	5:11 am	
☉⚹♃	7:09 am	
☽☍♃	10:05 am	
☉△☽	10:17 am	v/c

May

♑
♒

Thursday
2

♀⚼⚷	7:58 pm
☽→♒	9:43 pm

Beltane

♒

Friday
3

☽△♅	4:46 am
☽△♀	5:10 pm
☽☌♆	6:58 pm
♂☌♄	10:58 pm

All aspects in Pacific Daylight Time; add 3 hours for EDT; add 7 hours for GMT

Invoking Sisterhood

Beltane

Beltane is the cross-quarter fire festival halfway between Spring Equinox and Summer Solstice. Buds open, flowers color the green fields as the sun enters Taurus and the gibbous moon shines on young love. We join the Queen of May for a sexual dance around the maypole as lovers enact the fertility of Mother Earth. The maiden Goddess fertilizes Earth with her blood for the first time. Sexuality is experienced in all innocence without ownership or judgement. We honor our individual sexuality as source of life and creativity. We recognize the different parts of ourselves and unite them in *conjunctio*— sacred marriage.

Rejoice. Leap the fire with friends and lovers, releasing past hurts. Allow the warmth of the fire to open your heart. Celebrate the erotic as the sacred source of life. All acts of love and pleasure are the Goddess' rituals. Blessed be!

excerpt © Dánahy Sharonrose 1996, reprinted from We'Moon '97

For My Body Lent

For my body lent, one of a kind
from the library of forms
For this one, with
failing eyes and graceful legs
vulnerable vertebrae, deep hearing ears
This body, its age and streaming
The dreaming this body does
For this bonesack of a billion dancing
reactions
I bow in gratitude.
For being fed this day
by the elements that make me
For being lifted by the wind
like the white pine singing
outside my window
For last light caressing the shore
For five loons gliding by in a line
For the heron's whoop to its lifemate
For the scent of the peach in a bowl on
my table
For the material dearness of today
deep, deep thanks.
For my son's first word
For the taste of my lover's tongue
For longing and rapture and loss
For finding my place in the family
I am fiercely grateful.

¤ *Sue Silvermarie 2001*

Rising Spirit
© *Mara Friedman 1993*

May ——— ♄♄♄ Jumamosi ———————————

♒ Saturday
4

☉□☽ 12:16 am
☽△♄ 12:44 am
☽△♂ 12:49 am
☽✶♀ 7:05 am
♀△♅ 11:29 am

——— ☉☉☉ Jumapili ——— Waning Half Moon in ♒ Aquarius 12:16 am PDT

♒
♓ Sunday
5

☽♂♅ 5:46 am v/c
☽→♓ 8:46 am
☽□☿ 9:03 pm

May
Mai

♓

Monday
6

☽△♃	8:39 am
☽□♀	11:46 am
☽□♄	1:23 pm
☽□♂	4:27 pm
☉⚹☽	5:37 pm
☽□♀	7:10 pm v/c

© Cristina Sarasvati Carson 2000

Breast Cancer Study #2

♓
♈

Tuesday
7

♀♂♄	5:11 am
☉⚻♀	12:15 pm
☽ApG	12:18 pm
☽→♈	9:22 pm

♈

Wednesday
8

☽⚹♉	1:29 pm
♂☍♀	3:12 pm
☽⚹♆	7:31 pm
☽□♃	10:10 pm

♈

Thursday
9

☽⚹♄	2:36 am
☽⚹♀	7:12 am
☽△♀	7:37 am
☽⚹♂	8:37 am
♀☍♀	11:15 am

♈
♉

Friday
10

☿⚻♄	1:58 am
☽⚹♅	6:47 am v/c
☽→♉	9:32 am
♀♂♂	12:56 pm

Mama, I Tell You the Mountains Are Moving!

The women are coming together—by tens, by hundreds
out of the hospital beds, off of the X-ray tables
bald-headed women, one-breasted women
with bodies scarred and carved, pickled with poison to attack
the poison they breathed/they ate/their children sucked.
They are talking talking talking their stories
they are holding each other sobbing, they are beating the drums
they are drumming pounding drumming
they are laughing fiercely to be living
living, and fierce, and together.
And Mama, the breasted mountains are shaking.
I knew, when you lay broken and moaning
your chest flattened and stitched—brain, bone, lung on fire
I knew that someday the flaming women would erupt
someday they would drum the bedrock into motion
they would fault the poisonmakers, find each other with cadence
of love and fury. You would have loved to be among them, Mama.
I see you, and an army of your flat-chested ghost sisters
pounding pounding on the mantle of the world,
the drumskin is tight and thin, the living women match you
beat for beat— no wonder the cliffs are trembling.
I need not tell you, Mama, that the mountains are moving.

See Resources, page 188.   *excerpt © Bethroot Gwynn 2001*

♄♄♄ Samstag

♉

Saturday
11

☽□♆   7:11 am
☽✶♃ 10:37 am

☉☉☉ Sonntag

♉
♊

Sunday
12

☉☌☽   3:45 am
☽□♅   5:29 pm   v/c
☽→♊   8:04 pm

New Moon in ♉ Taurus 3:45 am PDT

Snake Priestess: Finding the Inner Serpent

I am a snake keeper and a snake dancer with my spiritual focus on the Great Mother Goddess. I dance with my royal pythons Nidaba and Monty, teaching and practicing healing of body, mind and spirit though sacred dance. Rather than choreographing a dance with the snakes, I allow the energy of my snakes as sentient beings to move me. I improvise with the snakes as my guides, my teachers, breathing deeply with them in a meditative state. It often feels as if the knowledge and wisdom of Gaia herself comes pouring through me. Filled with humility and quiet awe, I allow the gentle gliding of the snakes to dance me. It is beyond words, it is beyond performance, it is a healing.

Snakes are the greatest teachers of the breath. They breathe with their entire body. Every vertebra reverberates with life force of the breath. From the top of their heads to the tips of their tails, snakes inhale fully and deeply. It is a most exquisite meditation to hold a snake, synchronize my breathing with theirs, and feel the healing power of the breath. I practice yoga focusing on my spine as a snake, with poses embodying the waveform of snake energy. In Hinduism, shakti kundalini (or sacred life force) is seen as a cobra coiled at the base of the spine. When awakened, this serpent power moves up the spine, healing, clearing and transmuting energy blocks.

The serpent is not only my personal totem, but the universal totem for all women. Because the snake sheds its skin with open eyes, it witnesses its own death and rebirth. During a woman's menstruation, as she sheds the lining of her uterus, she too is bearing witness to death and rebirth. I believe that a Snake Priestess lives inside every woman. She is that purely instinctual aspect of the self. She is the key to our survival as healthy, vibrant, whole women during these radically shifting times. She is the power behind living in our truth.

VI. MEDITATE/CREATE

Moon VI: May 13–June 9

New Moon in ♉ Taurus: May 12; Sun in ♊ Gemini: May 20; Full Moon in ♐ Sagittarius: May 26

Snake Dancer
© *Ildiko Cziglenyi 1999*

May
Mei

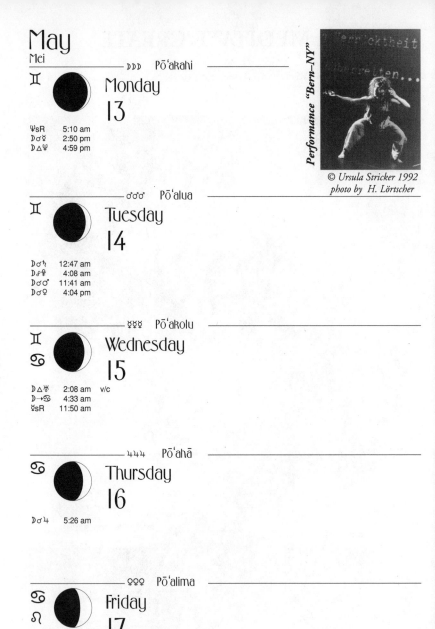

Performance "Bern–NY"

——))) Pō'akahi ——

♊

Monday
13

Ψsr 5:10 am
)♂☿ 2:50 pm
)△Ψ 4:59 pm

—— ♂♂♂ Pō'alua ——

♊

Tuesday
14

)♂♄ 12:47 am
)☌♀ 4:08 am
)♂♂ 11:41 am
)♂♀ 4:04 pm

—— ☿☿☿ Pō'akolu ——

♊
♋

Wednesday
15

)△♅ 2:08 am v/c
)→♋ 4:33 am
☿sr 11:50 am

—— ♃♃♃ Pō'ahā ——

♋

Thursday
16

)♂♃ 5:26 am

—— ♀♀♀ Pō'alima ——

♋
♌

Friday
17

⊙⚹) 4:27 am v/c
)→♌ 10:52 am

All aspects in Pacific Daylight Time; add 3 hours for EDT; add 7 hours for GMT

words and flame

i am a poet despite myself
i am a poet despite the hours for writing i never take
(i did not say i was a fine one) but crude, and aware
the occasional rough jewel of words that comes through my hands
is distinct enough not to go unread.
so, crafting and refining and laboring more would make me different
but would it suit my penchant for the raw?
i am a poet but do not resemble
those fiercely meticulous magicians of language
i am sloppy, accidental, channeling if for a brief spell.
clumsy, but i AM a poet
i must write this, for instance, lest i forget.
for i am not prolific in anything but conviction
and i'm no materialist which must explain
my indifference to hardly writing a thing!
and perhaps i squandered some poems
on the english major i love.
she's more stirred by my activism.
though magnificent political vision
should not look dissimilar to high art and sorcery.
there are great luminaries
but the rest of us may still claim art and struggle as ours.
radical politics and poetry reflect truth and propose transformation.
despite a paucity of aptitude, genius or discipline,
i must be a poet: words feed the fire of change
and i was born to ignite.

¤ *Elizabeth Roberts 1999*

ꜣꜣꜣ   Pōʻaono

♌

Saturday
18

☽✶♅	3:58 am
☽☌♆	6:11 am
☽✶♄	2:23 pm
☽△♀	4:17 pm

⊙⊙⊙   Lāpule

♌
♍

Sunday
19

☽✶♂	4:50 am	☽✶♀	1:34 pm	v/c
♀△♅	5:26 am	☽→♍	3:01 pm	
⊙□☽	12:42 pm	⊙□♅	3:25 pm	
☽☍♅	12:53 pm			

Waxing Half Moon in ♌ Leo 12:42 pm PDT

May
Majo

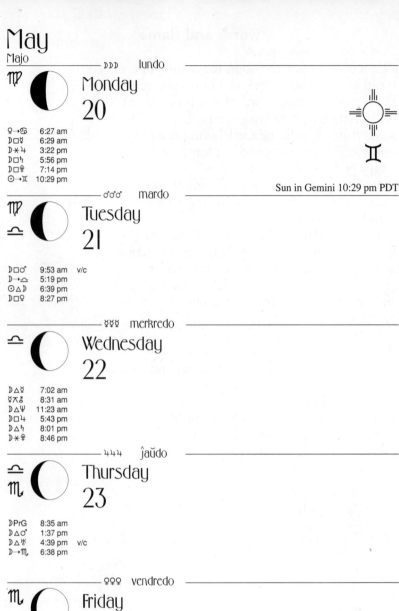

——))) lundo ——

♍

Monday
20

♀→♋ 6:27 am
)□♅ 6:29 am
)✳4 3:22 pm
)□♄ 5:56 pm
)□♀ 7:14 pm
☉→♊ 10:29 pm

♊

Sun in Gemini 10:29 pm PDT

—— ♂♂♂ mardo ——

♍
♎

Tuesday
21

)□♂ 9:53 am v/c
)→♎ 5:19 pm
☉△) 6:39 pm
)□♀ 8:27 pm

—— ☿☿☿ merkredo ——

♎

Wednesday
22

)△♅ 7:02 am
♅⊼♆ 8:31 am
)△♆ 11:23 am
)□4 5:43 pm
)△♄ 8:01 pm
)✳♀ 8:46 pm

—— 444 ĵaŭdo ——

♎
♏

Thursday
23

)PrG 8:35 am
)△♂ 1:37 pm
)△♅ 4:39 pm v/c
)→♏ 6:38 pm

—— ♀♀♀ vendredo ——

♏

Friday
24

)△♀ 2:09 am
)□♆ 12:39 pm
)△4 7:42 pm

All aspects in Pacific Daylight Time; add 3 hours for EDT; add 7 hours for GMT

Year at a Glance for ♊ GEMINI (May 20–June 21)

Confrontations and power struggles force you to stand up for the needs of a somewhat tentative, new personality. In the past few years you have completed or left behind many old interests and involvements, leaving you with only the indestructible essence of your being. In this process you are becoming more aware of how radical and progressive your philosophy of life is. Keep any projects you launch small. Allow them to develop slowly and organically. You need time alone and benefit from an uncluttered life. Nurturing yourself is particularly important as you may not feel very energetic this year. Be vigilant about getting adequate minerals. Take yourself seriously, but don't be too self-critical.

From mid-2001 through mid-2002 an increased faith that you will be provided for reflects an inner contentment and an enjoyment of the simple pleasures of life. However, do not rely totally upon faith to justify excessive expenditures.

In 2003, an offer of new work or perhaps even the sense of a calling emerges as an agent or catalyst bringing new ideas to the collective. Towards this, put your efforts into crafting an effective style or a setting which better conveys your genius. Your perennial hungry mind needs fodder or it may turn to negative thinking (especially in first half of the year). It would be to your advantage to take a course to improve communication skills, especially a progressive or experimental program. You contribute innovative ideas, concepts and insights to a favorite branch of knowledge or to the field of education itself. Literary gifts are most pronounced August 2001 onwards.

© *Gretchen Lawlor 2001*

© *Niamh Leonard 2000*

ħħħ   sabato

♏ ♐   ☽   Saturday
25

☽□♅   6:20 pm   v/c
ħ☍♀   7:33 pm
☽→♐   8:20 pm

☉☉☉   dimanĉo

♐   ◯   Sunday
26

☉☍☽   4:51 am
☽☍♄   6:51 am
♂△♅   9:30 am
☽⚹♆   2:50 pm

Full Moon in ♐ Sagittarius 4:51 am PDT
Appulse Lunar Eclipse 5:04 am PDT
Eclipse visible from the Americas, Russia, Australia and the Pacific Rim

May
Mei

──── ☽☽☽ Jumatatu ────

♐
♑

Monday
27

☉☌☿	12:09 am
♀☍♇	12:16 am
☽☌♀	12:29 am
☽☍♄	12:48 am
☿PrG	4:59 pm
☽⚹♅	9:49 pm
☽☍♂	11:40 pm v/c
☽→♑	11:54 pm

──── ♂♂♂ Jumanne ────

♑

Tuesday
28

♂→♋	4:43 am
☽☍♀	5:59 pm

──── ☿☿☿ Jumatano ────

♑

Wednesday
29

☽☍♃	4:46 am v/c
☉⚻♇	5:10 am
♀⚻♆	9:38 am

──── ♃♃♃ Alhamisi ────

♑
♒

Thursday
30

☽→♒	6:35 am
☽△☿	1:53 pm

──── ♀♀♀ Ijumaa ────

♒

Friday
31

☉△☽	1:00 am
♃⚻♀	2:57 am
☽☌♆	3:18 am
☽⚹♀	2:01 pm
☽△♄	3:46 pm

All aspects in Pacific Daylight Time; add 3 hours for EDT; add 7 hours for GMT

Juanita of the Highlands

I Am Woven

Sometimes I am woven
Into a safe soft still luminous cocoon
Made of moonbeams and loon feathers.

Other times I think I am the only weaver
Of sacred cloth for a hundred miles,
And I can't stop my shuttle.

But more and more now I remember
The sweet weaving around me
As I sit or lie dreaming.

Angels and old grandmothers weave me,
Wrap me, then hold me in a warm nest
When I close down my loom and rest.

¤ *Mary Feagan 2001*

ㅕㅕㅕ Jumamosi

♒︎
♓︎   Saturday
      1

☉△♆	6:38 am	
☽♂♅	2:19 pm	v/c
☽→♓	4:37 pm	
☽□♉	10:07 pm	
☽△♂	10:50 pm	

June

☉☉☉ Jumapili

♓︎   Sunday
      2

| ☉□☽ | 5:05 pm |
| ♅sR | 5:11 pm |

Waning Half Moon in ♓︎ Pisces 5:05 pm PDT

June
Juni

—— ☽☽☽ Montag ——

Monday
3

♓

♀⚹♇	12:06 am
☽□♀	1:22 am
☽△♀	1:30 am
☽△♃	2:44 am
☽□♄	3:58 am v/c
♀☌♃	4:12 pm

Half Moon Pose
© *Elizabeth Staber 2001*

—— ♂♂♂ Dienstag ——

Tuesday
4

♓
♈

☽→♈	4:51 am
☽ApG	5:58 am
☽⚹♉	8:44 am
☽□♂	2:42 pm

—— ☿☿☿ Mittwoch ——

Wednesday
5

♈

☽⚹♆	2:45 am
☉⚹☽	10:53 am
☽△♀	1:45 pm
☽□♃	4:19 pm
☽⚹♄	5:09 pm
☽□♀	8:41 pm

—— ♃♃♃ Donnerstag ——

Thursday
6

♈
♉

♀PrG	2:17 am
☽⚹♅	2:47 pm v/c
☽→♉	5:06 pm
☉☍♀	9:43 pm

—— ♀♀♀ Freitag ——

Friday
7

♉

☽⚹♂	6:10 am
☽□♆	2:26 pm

All aspects in Pacific Daylight Time; add 3 hours for EDT; add 7 hours for GMT

Deep Ecology Walking Meditation

May we worship in our bodies, not in spite of them. May we love the earth body without separation, making temples of our subtle gestures, our sparking hungers, our loamy thoughts. In motion, eyes open, we collaborate with space, time, gravity, energy. Embodied practice creates communion.

Stand with feet apart, eyes open, gaze soft. Shift weight, lift spine, drop belly to find yourself suspended on your bones, bridging earth and sky. Breathe in a continuous wave, round like moon tide. Rocking becomes walking, organically.

Bring your attention to points of exchange with the environment. Breathe in as trees breathe out. Move the air you press against. Warm the soil beneath your feet. Pass silence with the stones. Let sunlight or rainfall alter your skin. Trade breath, moisture, heat, nourishment and awareness with the pulsing, contiguous world. Know you are always doing exactly this.

As you walk, invoke what you love. Imagining creatures and places that make your heart sing and your body ache with joy or longing, send this love outward into your surroundings. Allow the object of your love to be a plant or animal or shaft of light; we are all made of the same stardust and love does not distinguish. Invoking those who love you, draw love in from the environment. Notice what changes . . . outside . . . inside . . . between.

Complete your walking meditation with thanks for the splendor into which we are born, and for that which was never born, never dies, yet endures. Walk in beauty. Blessed be.

¤ Jessica Montgomery 1999

ħħħ   Samstag

♉

Saturday
♉

☽⚹♃	4:38 am
☿sD	8:11 am
♂☍♄	10:24 am
☽⚹♀	2:03 pm

☉☉☉   Sonntag

♉
♊

Sunday
9

☽□♅	1:14 am	v/c
☽→♊	3:29 am	
☉♂♄	4:24 am	
☽♂♅	6:07 am	
♄ApG	8:25 am	
☽△♆	11:49 pm	

Pay the Mothers

Pool the money of all the
billionaires and multimillionaires
and with it pay all mothers each
the 400,000 dollars a year we earn
as mother, cook, maid, teacher,
trash collector, taxi service, mediator, nurse,
counselor, lawyer, waitress, coach,
bookkeeper, motivator, referee, consultant,
spiritual advisor, social director,
psychologist, interior designer,
general manager, domestic administrator.

Collect all the fame, awe, respect,
authority, and attention
lavished on star athletes and supermodels
and elevate mothers to that same pinnacle
of great deserving heights by
giving US therapeutic massage
when WE'RE injured, letting US sit the bench
at least a few minutes out of the game and
letting US cash in on OUR endorsements of
non-violence, whole foods, organic gardening,
attachment parenting and peace.

After all, we baked that apple pie—
Isn't it time we get a slice of it?

VII. MOTHER/NURTURE

Moon VII: June 10–July 7

New Moon in ♊ Gemini: June 10; Sun in ♋ Cancer: June 21; Full Moon in ♑ Capricorn: June 24

Future Medicine
char Cbear Freeman 1999

June
lune

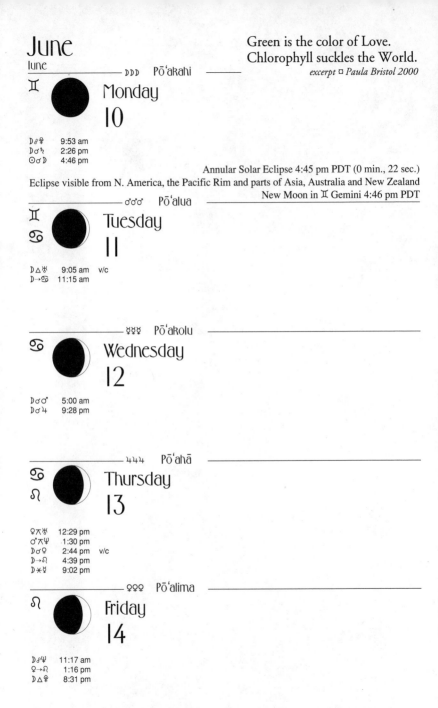

Green is the color of Love.
Chlorophyll suckles the World.
excerpt ¤ Paula Bristol 2000

——— ⅅⅅⅅ Pōʻakahi ———

♊

Monday
10

☽☌♀ 9:53 am
☽☌♄ 2:26 pm
☉☌☽ 4:46 pm

Annular Solar Eclipse 4:45 pm PDT (0 min., 22 sec.)
Eclipse visible from N. America, the Pacific Rim and parts of Asia, Australia and New Zealand
New Moon in ♊ Gemini 4:46 pm PDT

——— ♂♂♂ Pōʻalua ———

♊
♋

Tuesday
11

☽△♅ 9:05 am v/c
☽→♋ 11:15 am

——— ☿☿☿ Pōʻakolu ———

♋

Wednesday
12

☽☌♂ 5:00 am
☽☌♃ 9:28 pm

——— ♃♃♃ Pōʻahā ———

♋
♌

Thursday
13

♀⚹♅ 12:29 pm
♂⚹♆ 1:30 pm
☽☌♀ 2:44 pm v/c
☽→♌ 4:39 pm
☽⚹☿ 9:02 pm

——— ♀♀♀ Pōʻalima ———

♌

Friday
14

☽☍♆ 11:17 am
♀→♌ 1:16 pm
☽△♀ 8:31 pm

———

All aspects in Pacific Daylight Time; add 3 hours for EDT; add 7 hours for GMT

Unfolding This Season

As the kindness of verbena
expresses in excess
of that expected
As the clemency
of pansy utters far beyond
demands of fairness
May my mouth make the round
sound of mercy
Enough of pursed lips, the straight
line of judgement.

May dianthus and alyssum
be the syllables I chant
Let my mouth now sing
compassion in the shape
of a perfect peony
Like lilacs awaited
for years of spring,
unfolding finally this season,
may mercy from my mouth
ring into the world.

¤ Sue Silvermarie 2001

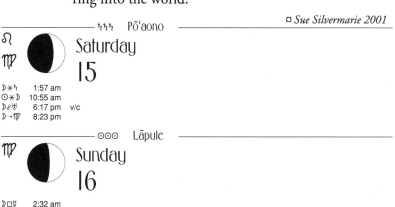

ħħħ　Pōʻaono

♌
♍

Saturday
15

☽✶ħ　　1:57 am
☉✶☽　10:55 am
☽☍♅　6:17 pm　v/c
☽→♍　8:23 pm

☉☉☉　Lāpule

♍

Sunday
16

☽□♅　2:32 am
☽✶♂　6:09 pm
☽□♀　11:34 pm

June
Junio

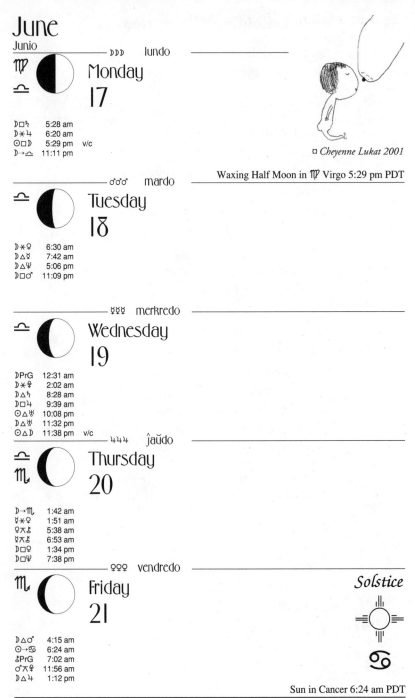

—————))) lundo —————

♍
♎
Monday
17

)□♄	5:28 am
)⚹♃	6:20 am
☉□)	5:29 am v/c
)→♎	11:11 pm

◻ *Cheyenne Lukat 2001*

Waxing Half Moon in ♍ Virgo 5:29 pm PDT

————— ♂♂♂ mardo —————

♎
Tuesday
18

)⚹♀	6:30 am
)△♅	7:42 am
)△♆	5:06 pm
)□♂	11:09 pm

————— ☿☿☿ merkredo —————

♎
Wednesday
19

)PrG	12:31 am
)⚹♀	2:02 am
)△♄	8:28 am
)□♃	9:39 am
☉△♅	10:08 pm
)△♇	11:32 pm
☉△)	11:38 pm v/c

————— ♃♃♃ ĵaŭdo —————

♎
♏
Thursday
20

)→♏	1:42 am
☿⚹♀	1:51 am
♀⚻♇	5:38 am
☿⚻♇	6:53 am
)□♀	1:34 pm
)□♆	7:38 pm

————— ♀♀♀ vendredo —————

♏
Friday
21

)△♂	4:15 am
☉→♋	6:24 am
♇PrG	7:02 am
♂⚻♀	11:56 am
)△♃	1:12 pm

Solstice

♋

Sun in Cancer 6:24 am PDT

All aspects in Pacific Daylight Time; add 3 hours for EDT; add 7 hours for GMT

Year at a Glance for ♋ CANCER (June 21–July 22)

Cancer born souls are in a profound transitional cycle of closure and completion in 2001 and 2002. You are shifting your focus from the worldly activities to which you have been devoted for the past 15 years. What is becoming more important to you is the quality of your personal life. In this process, an old personality structure is being left behind, but the new is not yet clearly formed. You may need help from friends, counselors, astrologers, to learn more about your capabilities, and help you focus on the new you that you are creating. You are moving towards a more intimate connection with your core self, as you concurrently disengage from the expectations of others. It is unlikely you will have to leave behind everything you know. Pick through your skills. Look for things which you still feel passion for; consider whether you could highlight or specialize in any of them. Pass the burden of responsibility for beloved projects to others so they don't wither.

From mid-2001 through mid-2002 you experience a self-confident burst of enthusiasm; use this jet stream to develop your specialties, to stretch yourself, to make new contacts. Health issues you encounter at this time will tend to have a strong psychological component. Listen to your body—it is nudging you to let go of old obligations, perhaps through crisis. If not originating from your own circumstances, changes may be required due to the situation of someone close to you. The spiritual dimensions of life become more compelling, providing a perspective from which your challenges will make sense and from which healing can take place.

© *Gretchen Lawlor 2001*

Nourishing Our Future
© *Christina Walczuk 1998*

ℏℏℏ sabato

♏ ♐ **Saturday**
22

☽□♅	2:27 am	v/c
☽→♐	4:42 am	
☽♂♉	8:20 pm	
☽△♀	9:29 pm	
☽✶♆	10:55 pm	

☉☉☉ dimanĉo

♐ **Sunday**
23

☽♂♀	8:06 am
♀♂♆	2:21 pm
☽♂ℏ	3:57 pm

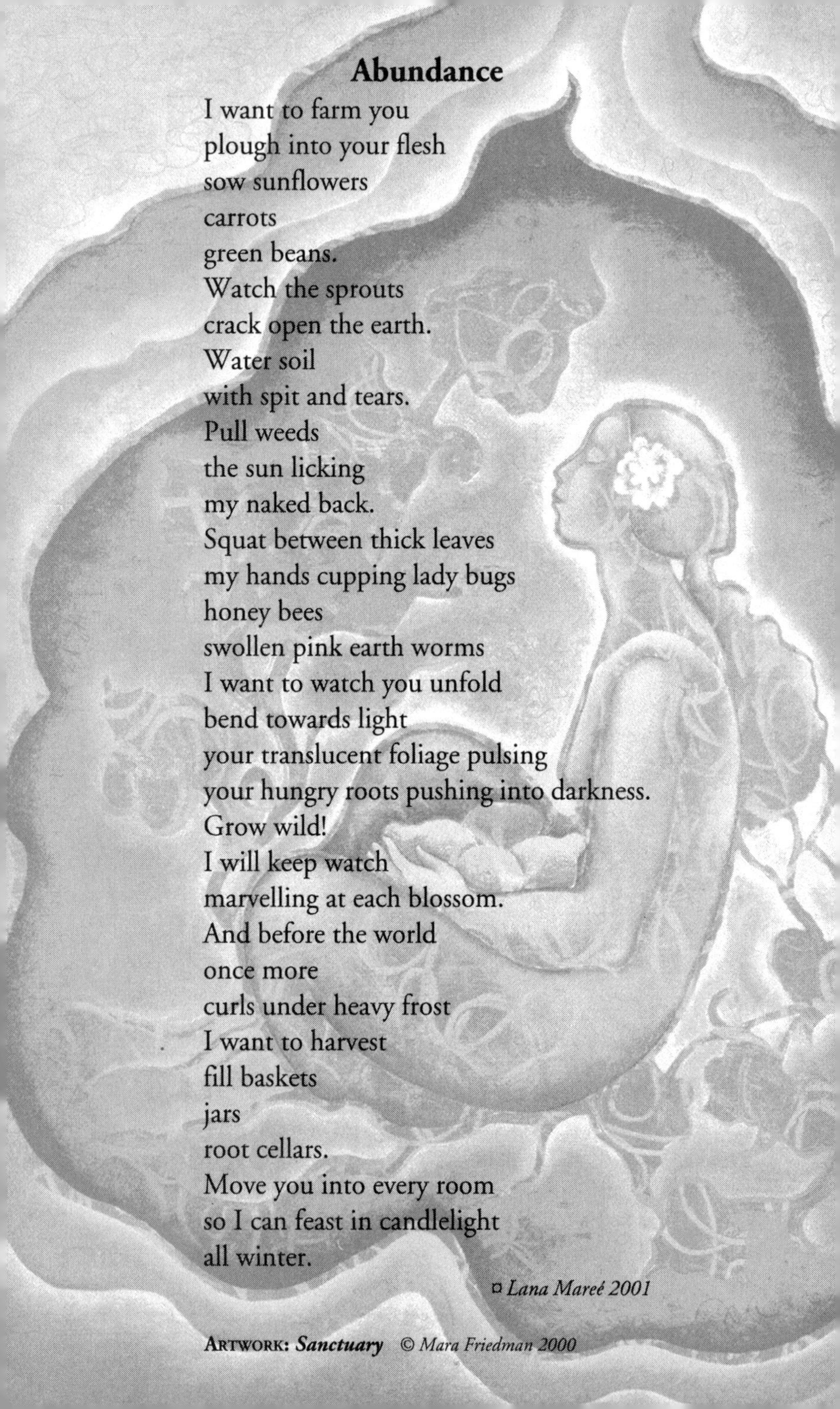

Abundance

I want to farm you
plough into your flesh
sow sunflowers
carrots
green beans.
Watch the sprouts
crack open the earth.
Water soil
with spit and tears.
Pull weeds
the sun licking
my naked back.
Squat between thick leaves
my hands cupping lady bugs
honey bees
swollen pink earth worms
I want to watch you unfold
bend towards light
your translucent foliage pulsing
your hungry roots pushing into darkness.
Grow wild!
I will keep watch
marvelling at each blossom.
And before the world
once more
curls under heavy frost
I want to harvest
fill baskets
jars
root cellars.
Move you into every room
so I can feast in candlelight
all winter.

¤ *Lana Mareé 2001*

ARTWORK: ***Sanctuary***   © *Mara Friedman 2000*

© *Sarah Teofanov 1998*

Summer Solstice

In many cultures, rituals are performed to illustrate the Sun's effect on Earth life, especially around Summer Solstice, the longest day of the year. In some countries the Sun is a Goddess. For example, in Egypt the Goddess Hathor is addressed as "the fiery one, She who was never created." In Arabia She is called Attar of Al-lat, the Torch of the Gods. The Sun Goddess is named Anyanwu by the Ibo of Nigeria and Indombe, the blazing heat, in Zaire. Akewa is Her name among the Toba people of Argentina. And the rising sun, "the ruler of all the deities," is the Goddess Amaterasu of Japan. Oshun, the Yoruba river maiden is the daughter of the sun, and Mary the mother of Jesus is the "woman clothed with the sun." She is Sunna to the Celts, and to the Inuit, She is Sun sister.

In summer we strip naked, plunge into cool water and enjoy the beauty of the night sky.

© *Luisah Teish 1997, reprinted from* We'Moon '98, *excerpted from* Carnival of the Spirit

June

Juni

─────))) Jumatatu ─────────────────────

♐
♑

Monday
24

☿△♆ 5:00 am
)✶⛢ 6:38 am   v/c
)→♑ 9:01 am
☉☍) 2:42 pm

Appulse Lunar Eclipse 2:23 pm PDT
Eclipse visible from S. America, Europe, Africa, Asia and Australia
Full Moon in ♑ Capricorn 2:42 pm PDT

───── ♂♂♂ Jumanne ─────────────────────

♑

Tuesday
25

)☍♂ 6:40 pm

───── ☿☿☿ Jumatano ─────────────────────

♑
♒

Wednesday
26

)☍♃ 12:37 am   v/c
)→♒ 3:36 pm

───── ♃♃♃ Alhamisi ─────────────────────

♒

Thursday
27

)♂♆ 11:18 am
☉☍♤ 5:19 pm
)△⛢ 7:56 pm
)☍♀ 8:52 pm
)✶♀ 9:20 pm

───── ♀♀♀ Ijumaa ─────────────────────

♒

Friday
28

♀△♀ 1:49 am
)△♄ 7:20 am
☿☍♀ 8:37 am
)♂⛢ 10:12 pm   v/c

All aspects in Pacific Daylight Time; add 3 hours for EDT; add 7 hours for GMT

Hot Love

All my love poured
into those meals: exotic
flavors, painstakingly
learned in alien marketplaces
and alien tongues:
Quechua, Aymara, Urdu.
Piles of unfamiliar powders:
achiote and haldi, blood-
red and yellow, sizzled under
the striped awnings in heat
and cracking cold.

All my love, energy,
time: bent ardently over my
charcoal fires, my hearth
of twigs or clay,
to feed you every succulent
sacrifice, the taste
of each new world: eaten
with sighs, every finger licked
clean: Can you still taste
my love?

¤ *Carol Sawyer 1999*

Cooking Goddess
© *Anna Oneglia 1995*

───── ♄♄♄ Jumamosi ─────

≈
♓ ☽ Saturday
29

☽→♓   1:00 am
☿✶♀   3:16 pm
☉△☽   4:52 pm

───── ☉☉☉ Jumapili ─────

♓ ☽ Sunday
30

☽□♀   8:02 am
☽□☿   2:37 pm
☽□♄   7:11 pm
☽△♂   8:37 pm
☽△♃ 10:43 pm   v/c

July
Juli

☽☽☽ Montag

♓
♈

Monday
1

☽→♈ 12:49 pm

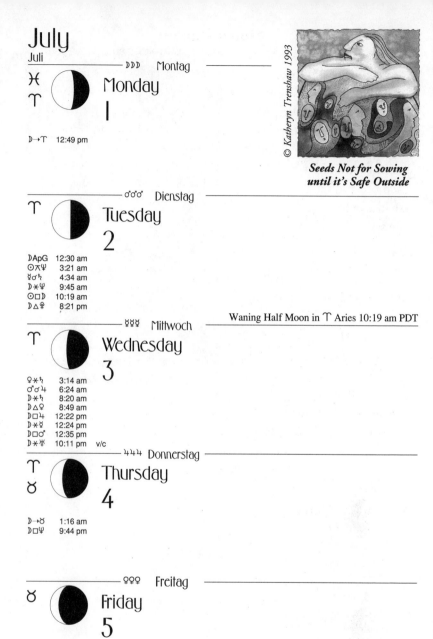

© Katheryn Trenshaw 1993

Seeds Not for Sowing until it's Safe Outside

♂♂♂ Dienstag

♈

Tuesday
2

☽ApG 12:30 am
☉⊼♆ 3:21 am
☿☌♄ 4:34 am
☽⚹♆ 9:45 am
☉□☽ 10:19 am
☽△♇ 8:21 pm

Waning Half Moon in ♈ Aries 10:19 am PDT

☿☿☿ Mittwoch

♈

Wednesday
3

♀⚹♄ 3:14 am
♂☌♃ 6:24 am
☽⚹♄ 8:20 am
☽△♀ 8:49 am
☽□♃ 12:22 pm
☽⚹☿ 12:24 pm
☽□♂ 12:35 pm
☽⚹♅ 10:11 pm v/c

♃♃♃ Donnerstag

♈
♉

Thursday
4

☽→♉ 1:16 am
☽□♆ 9:44 pm

♀♀♀ Freitag

♉

Friday
5

☉⚹☽ 3:31 am

All aspects in Pacific Daylight Time; add 3 hours for EDT; add 7 hours for GMT

Stolen Harvest

Over the past two decades every issue I have been engaged in as an ecological activist and organic intellectual has revealed that what the industrial economy calls *growth* is really a form of theft from nature and people. These thefts have only stepped up since the advent of the globalized economy . . . has legalized corporate growth based on harvests stolen from nature and people . . .

[An international meeting in 1987] made it clear that the giant chemical companies [were] repositioning themselves as *life sciences* companies . . . to control agriculture through patents, genetic engineering and mergers. At that meeting, I decided I would dedicate the next decade of my life to finding ways to prevent monopolies on life and living resources, both through resistance and by building creative alternatives.

The first step I took was to start Navadanya, a movement for saving seed, to protect biodiversity and to keep seed and agriculture free of monopoly control. The Navdanya family has started 16 community seed banks in six states in India, has thousands of members who conserve biodiversity, practice chemical-free agriculture, and have taken a pledge to continue to save and share the seeds and biodiversity they have received as gifts from nature and their ancestors. Navdanya's commitment to saving seed means we cannot cooperate with patent laws, which make seed-saving a crime.

© Vandana Shiva 2000, excerpted and reprinted with permission from Stolen Harvest: The Hijacking of the Global Food Supply *(South End Press)*
See Resources, page 188.

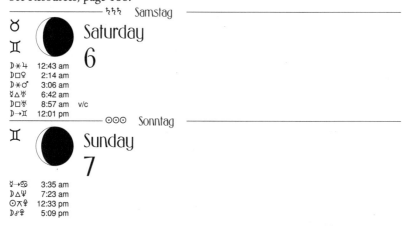

Mandala Dance of the 21 Praises of Tara

From around the globe, we gather.
In a pulsing golden spiral, we dance.
In moving meditation, we embody the goddess.
Singing her mantras,
We invoke her
Within ourselves
And within the world.
Woman to Woman,
We empower one another.
Women to World,
We bring forth blessing,
As archaic memories swell
In sacred recognition of this divine responsibility.

© *Anahata*
Iradah 2000

Acknowledging the dignity and capability of all women to accomplish the highest spiritual attainment, the Mandala Dance of the 21 Praises of Tara is an inspiration to each of us to live our highest expression of humanity and to walk in wisdom and compassion. Gathering women of all backgrounds, Tara Dhatu brings the ancient meditations of the Goddess Tara, still chanted by Tibetans, into active embodiment through sacred dance. Witnessed and blessed by esteemed teachers from many traditions, this practice has been performed in communities and sacred sites around the world.

In Tibetan Buddhist tradition, the Goddess Tara, born from the green syllable *tam*, appeared in the center of a lotus vowing to remain in the body of a woman until all beings were free from suffering. Swift to go to all who call out to her, she is revered as the Mother of all things. The embodiment of wisdom and compassion, she is imbued with 21 qualities including such divine virtues as sublime intelligence, radiant health, invincible courage, creative wisdom, ferocious compassion, irresistible truth and complete enlightenment.

Indigenous women, delegates of many organizations and women from more than twenty-one nations gathered in the fall of 2001 on a Pilgrimage of Peace led by Prema Dasara and Anahata Iradah to dance the Mandala Dance of the 21 Praises of Tara in India and Nepal. The women formed moving human mandalas through which they birthed the 21 qualities of the Goddess Tara within themselves and into the world.   □ *Jennifer Case 2000*

*See Resources, page 188.

VIII. CIRCLE/INVOKE

Moon VIII: July 8–August 4

New Moon in ♋ Cancer: July 10; Sun in ♌ Leo: July 23; Full Moon in ♒ Aquarius: July 24

Matrix
© *Diane Porter Goff 1993*

July
Iulai

♊
♋

Monday
8

☽☌♄	5:24 am	
☽⚹♀	3:40 pm	
☽△♅	4:37 pm	v/c
☽→♋	7:36 pm	

Prayer Flag Ritual
© Jan McLaughlin 2000

———— ♂♂♂ Pō'alua ————

♋

Tuesday
9

☽☌☿	2:14 am
♀☍♅	2:38 am
☿☍♇	10:38 pm

———— ☿☿☿ Pō'akolu ————

♋

Wednesday
10

☉☌☽	3:26 am	
♀→♍	2:09 pm	
☽☌♃	3:48 pm	
♂⚻♅	4:23 pm	
☽☌♂	9:25 pm	v/c

New Moon in ♋ Cancer 3:26 am PDT

———— ♃♃♃ Pō'ahā ————

♋
♌

Thursday
11

| ☽→♌ | 12:08 am |
| ☽☍♆ | 5:22 pm |

———— ♀♀♀ Pō'alima ————

♌

Friday
12

☽△♀	2:14 am	
☿⚻♆	7:00 am	
☽⚹♄	2:28 pm	
☽☍♅	11:42 pm	v/c

All aspects in Pacific Daylight Time; add 3 hours for EDT; add 7 hours for GMT

Prayer Flag Ritual

Down at the creek, Canadian sculptress Mitch Spiralstone was intrigued with mounds of rocks and boulders, monuments of greed left by previous plunderers of the earth. Nearly a century after the Placer miners, the Earth Mother stood barren, stark. But the 1995 dyke art camp (DARE—Dyke Art Retreat Encampment) was in session!

Mitch spoke of trying to create some beauty out of the lifeless rock mound. That reminded Boand of coming across ancient sacred spots in England—long forgotten—marked by carvings in a rock or paintings in a cave. We talked of creating something sacred on the mound. I had heard of prayer flags in the Buddhist tradition; the idea of the prayer-flag ritual was birthed and distilled. The larger group adopted it as the group project for our tribal gathering.

Each artist at the camp created a prayer flag, a spiritual symbol to implore the powers of the great mother of us all to heal the earth and to heal us. At the end of the camp, as part of our closing circle, we shared our flags and explained what each symbolized. Then we lined up chronologically, ending with the oldest crone, and went in somber, chanting procession down the hill through spirals Mitch had created of rock. On the crest of the mound, we cast the circle and blessed the spot. We sang and chanted and said our prayers to the Goddess as we anchored our prayer flags in the center of our circle.

© *Jan McLaughlin 2000*

See Resources page 188.

ϞϞϞ   Pōʻaono

♌
♍

Saturday
13

☽→♍	2:41 am
☽☌♀	7:49 am
♂→♌	8:23 am

☉☉☉   Lāpule

♍

Sunday
14

☽✶♅	1:43 am	☽□♄	4:53 pm
☽□♀	4:15 am	♅⊼♀	6:55 pm
☽PrG	6:22 am	☽✶♃	10:08 pm v/c
☉✶☽	3:49 pm		

July
Julio

By Moon Dark & Moon Bright
In Lightest Heart & Inner Night
We weave the Web
to set things right.

¤ *Patricia Worth 2000*

☽☽☽ lundo

♍ ♎

Monday
15

♀△⚷ 2:07 am
☽→♎ 4:39 am
☽✶♂ 6:44 am
☽△♆ 9:27 pm

♂♂♂ mardo

♎

Tuesday
16

☽✶♇ 6:21 am
☽□☿ 12:38 pm
☽△♄ 7:39 pm
☉□☽ 9:47 pm

Waxing Half Moon in ♎ Libra 9:47 pm PDT

☿☿☿ merkredo

♎ ♏

Wednesday
17

☽□♃ 1:23 am
☽△♅ 3:58 am v/c
☽→♏ 7:13 am
☽□♂ 11:45 am
☽✶♀ 9:11 pm

♃♃♃ ĵaŭdo

♏

Thursday
18

☽□♆ 12:17 am

♀♀♀ vendredo

♏ ♐

Friday
19

☽△☿ 1:22 am
☉△☽ 5:11 am
☽△♃ 5:54 am
☽□♅ 7:35 am v/c
☽→♐ 11:02 am
♀⚻♆ 11:26 am
☽△♂ 6:16 pm
☉☌♃ 6:19 pm

All aspects in Pacific Daylight Time; add 3 hours for EDT; add 7 hours for GMT

© Lisa de St. Croix 2000

Circling

♐ Saturday
20

☽✶♆	4:30 am	☉⊼♅	2:34 pm
☽□♀	6:03 am	☿⊼♅	4:51 pm
♀♂♃	9:24 am	♂⊼♇	5:09 pm
☽♂♀	1:57 pm	☉♂♂	6:47 pm

⊙⊙⊙ dimanĉo

♐
♑ Sunday
21

♃ApG	4:18 am	
☽♂♄	5:05 am	
☽✶♅	12:44 pm	v/c
☿→♌	3:41 pm	
☽→♑	4:26 pm	

MOON VIII   119

July
Julai

♑

Monday
22

☽△♀ 5:03 pm
☉→♌ 5:15 pm

♌

Sun in Leo 5:15 pm PDT

♑
♒

Tuesday
23

♃⊼♅ 12:18 am
☿ApG 5:03 pm
☿⊼♇ 7:48 pm
☽♂♃ 8:05 pm   v/c
☽→♒ 11:40 pm

♒

Wednesday
24

☉♂☽ 2:07 am
♀□♀ 5:40 am
☽♂♉ 10:39 am
☽♂♂ 1:12 pm
☽♂♆ 6:10 pm

Lunar Lammas
Full Moon in ♒ Aquarius 2:07 am PDT

♒

Thursday
25

☽⚹♀ 4:23 am
☿♂♂ 8:20 am
☽△♄ 9:52 pm

♒
♓

Friday
26

☽♂♅ 4:47 am   v/c
☿♂♆ 8:40 am
☽→♓ 9:04 am

All aspects in Pacific Daylight Time; add 3 hours for EDT; add 7 hours for GMT

Year at a Glance for ♌ LEO (July 22–August 22)

A crisis this year relating to your image or reputation reveals some stale and constrictive mindsets. Are your goals and aspirations big enough? This is a good year to make plans for the future, to strategize ways to bring your inspirations to life. Let go of some old dream in the first half of the year—it is no longer appropriate. Free up your hours so there is space for something new to enter, then watch/pray for inspiration. New passions and opportunities will emerge in the second half of this year. If you have prepared, you can meet them with a flood of confident energy.

Friends made this year will stay in your life for a long time; your tastes may lean towards older or more serious individuals. Old friends reenter your life. People are impressed with your display of organizational powers and self-confidence; you could be offered a leadership role—take it.

Love, artistry and children are all intense and challenging in 2002, though the insights provided by the turmoil are profound. Children refuse to carry your dreams and set off on their own. Lovers could develop rebellious tendencies, but ah, your art is passionate and so satisfying. You could be famous this year.

For the last few years you may have experienced some obsessiveness in relationships, an attraction to unusual people, and a difficulty settling into any ordinary routine together. If you have suffered a string of explosive affairs, you may be holding on too tightly. Abandon the focus upon dependable comfort, and open yourself instead to electrifying collaborations and soulful spirit mates who burst your life open with erratic flair.

© *Gretchen Lawlor 2001*

If I Were a Little Bird
© *Jennifer Beam 2001*

————— ♄♄♄ Jumamosi —————

♓

Saturday
27

☉⚹♟	7:10 am
☽□♀	2:52 pm
☽☌♀	11:03 pm

————— ☉☉☉ Jumapili —————

♓
♈

Sunday
28

☽□♄	9:37 am	
♂☌♅	11:32 am	
☽△♃	7:01 pm	v/c
☽→♈	8:38 pm	

July/August
Juli/August

─── ☽☽☽ Montag ───

♈ **Monday**
29

☿△♀	1:11 am
☉△☽	9:30 am
☽✶♆	4:09 pm
☽△♂	5:51 pm
☽ApG	6:36 pm

Summer Celebration
☐ *Shoshana Rothaizer 1989*

─── ♂♂♂ Dienstag ───

♈ **Tuesday**
30

☽△♀	3:08 am
☽△♅	8:14 am
☽✶♄	10:45 pm

─── ☿☿☿ Mittwoch ───

♈
♉ **Wednesday**
31

☽✶♅	4:28 am	
☽□♃	8:48 am	v/c
☽→♉	9:17 am	

─── ♃♃♃ Donnerstag ───

♉ **Thursday**
1

August

☉□☽	3:22 am
☽□♆	4:34 am
☽□♂	9:46 am
♆PrG	10:03 am
♃→♌	10:20 am
☉☌♆	5:57 pm

Waning Half Moon in ♉ Taurus 3:22 am PDT

─── ♀♀♀ Freitag ───

Lammas

♉
♊ **Friday**
2

☽□♅	7:30 am	
♀□♄	9:10 am	
☽△♀	11:18 am	
☽□♅	3:58 pm	v/c
☽→♊	8:46 pm	
☽✶♃	9:24 pm	

All aspects in Pacific Daylight Time; add 3 hours for EDT; add 7 hours for GMT

Watermelons in the Shade*

*at the Michigan Women's Music Festival   □ *Shoshana Rothaizer 1988*

Lammas

Lammas is a celebration of the Harvest Mother and the fruits and harvest of the life force. The great Lammas feasts traditionally lasted for one month—fifteen days before August 1st and fifteen days after. Fermentations (cider and beer) were seen as the essence of germination, a kind of watery fire of life, and were used as a ritual element at the feasts. Cooking fires were honored as the transformative power of fire and water together. Harvesting took place with the waning moon. The first fruits were offered to the Earth Mother.

Fires were lit on Lammas mounds like Silbury Hill; at Avebury people gathered to feel the Earth Mother give birth to her harvest child in conjunction with the Moon and her waters. This is the time when the Goddess withdraws into the mounds and the earth. The forces which began to rise out of the earth at Imbolc now return.

Lammas is a time of abundance and surplus of food. The cross quarter points represent change in manifest energy. And so nature ripens; everything is peaking in its growth. Green turns to gold. Summer feels as if it will last forever but from here this peak of climax and growth are the first signs of death. We must bear in mind the future and hard times of winter. It is time to lay in store the things we will need.   □ *Glennie Kindred 1991, reprinted from* We'Moon '99

Dancing Priestesses

This Time We Make the Fire of Love
*Goddess Conference, Glastonbury**

All around the wary town the gathered women
carry Lammas fire. It's in their pockets
and their little satin bags, small sparks innocent
as petals leaving spangles on the grass.
Some have rucksacks full of slithery flames that escape
in snakey tendrils down their backs, some
wear fiery sun-circles on their hands
rubies, garnets glint like darts.

The women carry fire in their bodies, in red wombs
and red rivers, in young muscles full of kundalini grace,
in soft wrinkled skins brimmed with burning water
and a hundred scarlet fireheaded women
set little bonfires bobbing in the street
so the town quivers at the dangers of ignition.

Light gives away only part of their secrets
in a gleam here and there, or that look, as if
within the eye's deep pool a goddess quickly
dazzled, and smiled as she lit the heart.

And these fiery loving women walk around
astonishing the tourists, the pilgrims and the town wives:
Of, course, they say, *of course we carry fire,
we have always done so: fire of Inanna, fire of Diana
fire of Bride, we are all sacred fireholders—
Hey lady—slip inside yourself and see.*

* See Resources, page 188.   © *Rose Flint 2001*

She Laughed When I Asked Her How To Priestess

I asked my inner goddess,
wise playful thing that she is,
what it meant for me to priestess,
and she burst into laughter.
Not unkindly, you understand,
she was gentle,
but thoroughly amused.
"Oh! why does your head like to
go get so complicated?"
That's what her deep laughter said.
"You ask me how to priestess?!
Go to a mirror, any kind,
extend love to yourself.
Grounded from there,
you will priestess in all you do."

excerpt ¤ Nicola Holmes 2000

Invoking the Directions
© Marj Greenhut 1993

August

♄♄♄   Samstag

♊

Saturday
3

☿✶♄	9:11 am
☽△♆	3:04 pm
☉✶☽	6:52 pm
☽✶♂	11:13 pm

☉☉☉   Sonntag

♊

Sunday
4

☽☍♀	1:26 am
♀⊼♅	3:45 pm
☿⚹♅	3:59 pm
☽♂♄	8:28 pm

August
'Aukake

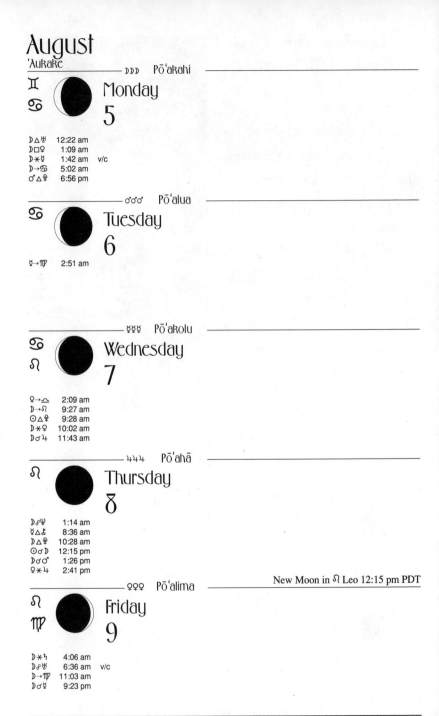

───── ☽☽☽ Pō'akahi ──────────────────

♊
♋

Monday
5

☽△♅ 12:22 am
☽□♀ 1:09 am
☽⚹♉ 1:42 am   v/c
☽→♋ 5:02 am
♂△♀ 6:56 pm

───── ♂♂♂ Pō'alua ──────────────────

♋

Tuesday
6

☿→♍ 2:51 am

───── ☿☿☿ Pō'akolu ──────────────────

♋
♌

Wednesday
7

♀→♎ 2:09 am
☽→♌ 9:27 am
☉△♀ 9:28 am
☽⚹♀ 10:02 am
☽♂♃ 11:43 am

───── ♃♃♃ Pō'ahā ──────────────────

♌

Thursday
8

☽☍♆ 1:14 am
☿△♇ 8:36 am
☽△♇ 10:28 am
☉♂☽ 12:15 pm
☽♂♂ 1:26 pm
♀⚹♃ 2:41 pm

───── ♀♀♀ Pō'alima ──── New Moon in ♌ Leo 12:15 pm PDT

♌
♍

Friday
9

☽⚹♄ 4:06 am
☽☍♅ 6:36 am   v/c
☽→♍ 11:03 am
☽♂☿ 9:23 pm

──

All aspects in Pacific Daylight Time; add 3 hours for EDT; add 7 hours for GMT

Magical Activism

*Into the fiery
cauldron
of transformation
we banish the
WTO and all that
is harmful to the
Earth and Her
inhabitants.
Dancing
widdershins,
we cast our spell.*

© photo by D. Summerville 1999

There were witches at work during the WTO protests in Seattle. We went to join thousands of people to voice our opposition to corporate globalization and to do a little magic! We grounded ourselves and cast a circle of protection, invoking the elements to assist us in our important work. We chanted and sang, shook rattles and burned incense. A lot of energy moved that day! The WTO meetings were unsuccessful, and many people were inspired to take action and work for a better world. Our magic helped to create change!

☐ *Diana Gardener 2001*

♍

ħħħ Pōʻaono

Saturday
10

☽□♀	11:17 am
☉♂♂	3:17 pm
☽PrG	4:42 pm
♀□♃	4:44 pm

♍
♎

☉☉☉ Lāpule

Sunday
11

☽□ħ	5:01 am	v/c
☽→♎	11:38 am	
☽✶♃	3:17 pm	
☿⊼♅	5:11 pm	
☽♂♀	7:34 pm	

A Woman In China Wails

I wake up each morning
    to muffled sobs.
A woman in China
    wailing at the base of my skull.
She spins
    cobweb threads
    intertwining the folds of my cerebrum
    into a point of interception
    between
        strength and submission
Her endurance
    pounds behind my forehead
        to remind me of her will.
    A silence we share
        of necessity
        custom and power
        a tradition of power blinding
            Western thought.
My woman hobbles through my brain
    on the crumpled knobs
        of her bound feet
    bending as I do
        our backs stiff
        with the burden of dual culture
But in the knowing
    of her gaze emitted through my eyes
I sense
    the wisdom of her calloused hands
    painted to my fingertips
And the unspoken certainty
    of her formlessness
    the dark sobbing
        constricting my heart
        into a diamond
        of love, hatred, and
            strength.

IX. LIBERATE/EMPOWER

Moon IX: August 8–September 6

New Moon in ♌ Leo: Aug. 8; Full Moon in ♒ Aquarius: Aug. 22; Sun in ♍ Virgo: Aug. 23;

Beasts in Red and Black
© Cora Yee 1990

August
Aŭgusto

Bikini Girl Tri-athletes—Mosaic Floor—3rd Century C.E. Sicily
© *Eaglehawk 2001*

DDD lundo

♎ ## Monday
12

☽△♆	2:47 am
☽✶♀	12:02 pm
☽✶♂	7:32 pm
☉✶☽	8:46 pm

♂♂♂ mardo

♎ ♏ ## Tuesday
13

☽△♄	6:32 am	
☽△♅	8:11 am	v/c
☽→♏	1:01 pm	
☽□♃	5:32 pm	

☿☿☿ merkredo

♏ ## Wednesday
14

☽□♆	4:36 am
♂ApG	4:50 am
☽✶☿	12:06 pm

♃♃♃ ĵaŭdo

♏ ♐ ## Thursday
15

☽□♂	12:34 am	
☉□☽	3:12 am	
☿□♀	8:29 am	
☽□♅	11:13 am	v/c
☽→♐	4:25 pm	
☽△♃	10:00 pm	

Waxing Half Moon in ♏ Scorpio 3:12 am PDT

♀♀♀ vendredo

♐ ## Friday
16

♀△♆	2:01 am
☽✶♆	8:40 am
☽✶♀	9:12 am
☽☌♀	6:54 pm
☽□♅	11:12 pm

All aspects in Pacific Daylight Time; add 3 hours for EDT; add 7 hours for GMT

Women Run Wild

□ *Nicola Holmes 2000*

This is a YES! place
Love is a YES!
            Not a maybe
            Or a will see
            Or a if you do this & this & this
It's a brisk, clear water, earth, air
            And fire paradise!
We are whole and alive
            And brilliant and beautiful
And YES!!!

□ *Joanie Levine 2000*

───── ♄♄♄   sabato ─────

Saturday
17

☽△♂	8:22 am	
♃⊼♇	12:18 pm	
☉△☽	12:37 pm	
☽☌♄	3:53 pm	
☽✳♅	4:39 pm	v/c
☽→♑	10:15 pm	

───── ☉☉☉   dimanĉo ─────

Sunday
18

| ♅PrG | 7:18 pm |
| ☽□♀ | 8:18 pm |

August
Agosti

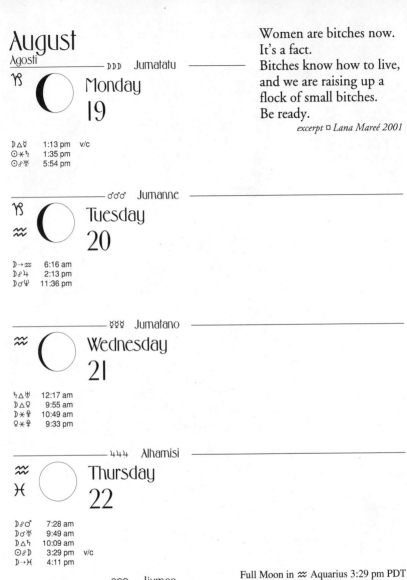

───── ⟩⟩⟩ Jumatatu ─────

♑ **Monday**

19

☽△☿ 1:13 pm v/c
☉✶♄ 1:35 pm
☉☌♅ 5:54 pm

───── ♂♂♂ Jumanne ─────

♑
♒ **Tuesday**

20

☽→♒ 6:16 am
☽☍♃ 2:13 pm
☽☌♆ 11:36 pm

───── ☿☿☿ Jumatano ─────

♒ **Wednesday**

21

♄△♅ 12:17 am
☽△♀ 9:55 am
☽✶♀ 10:49 am
♀✶♀ 9:33 pm

───── ♃♃♃ Alhamisi ─────

♒
♓ **Thursday**

22

☽☍♂ 7:28 am
☽☌♅ 9:49 am
☽△♄ 10:09 am
☉☍☽ 3:29 pm v/c
☽→♓ 4:11 pm

───── ♀♀♀ Ijumaa ─────

♓ **Friday**

23

☉→♍ 12:17 am
☿⚹♅ 8:52 pm
☽□♀ 9:36 pm

Women are bitches now.
It's a fact.
Bitches know how to live,
and we are raising up a
flock of small bitches.
Be ready.

excerpt ¤ Lana Mareé 2001

Full Moon in ♒ Aquarius 3:29 pm PDT

♍

Sun in Virgo 12:17 am PDT

All aspects in Pacific Daylight Time; add 3 hours for EDT; add 7 hours for GMT

Year at a Glance for ♍ VIRGO (Aug. 22–Sept.22)

Expect acclaim this year. You could reach a pinnacle of ambitions, especially in your capacity as Virgo as wordsmith or spokesperson. You may have found a great niche, after striving for a number of years. Your imagination and capacity to innovate in tools or techniques have been recently noticed by those in positions of authority, who are now opening doors to your success.

This external recognition parallels an emotional coming of age. Plumb the depths of your soul, question your attitudes towards power. Step away from the influence of an old authority figure, be it parent, boss, mentor or mate. Through this assertive action, you discover an inner power and a deep seated stability. This may not be without some crisis. If you experience unusual or even difficult to diagnose health problems, a general malaise or even bouts of despair, you are on the right track; an old attitude is dragging you down and needs to be abandoned. A subconscious dependence or subservience is challenged and transformed as you step into your own authority.

In the first half of the year, professional connections as well as clubs or organizations of peers will help you progress and bring you a sense of companionship. The support of important people helps in the realization of your plans. Enjoy these fruits of your labors, though be alert for a yearning for new horizons. In the second half of the year, be willing to surrender some old interests or involvements in order to prepare for new life looming on your horizons. In 2003, important people will rocket into your life, unexpected and inspiring experiences will propel you forward.

© *Gretchen Lawlor 2001*

Bitch Goddess
© *Anna Oneglia 1995*

──────── ♄♄♄ Jumamosi ────────

♓ ○ Saturday
24

♂☍♅	2:29 am	
♉□♄	3:58 am	
♂⚹♄	6:40 pm	
☽□♄	10:00 pm	
☽☍♉	11:57 pm	v/c

──────── ☉☉☉ Jumapili ────────

♓
♈ ○ Sunday
25

☽→♈	3:47 am	
☽△♃	2:20 pm	
☽⚹♆	9:51 pm	

August

August

─────))) Montag ─────

♈

Monday
26

♀sD	3:59 am
☽△♀	9:53 am
☽ApG	10:43 am
☉△♅	10:52 am
☿→♎	2:10 pm
☽☍♀	7:18 pm

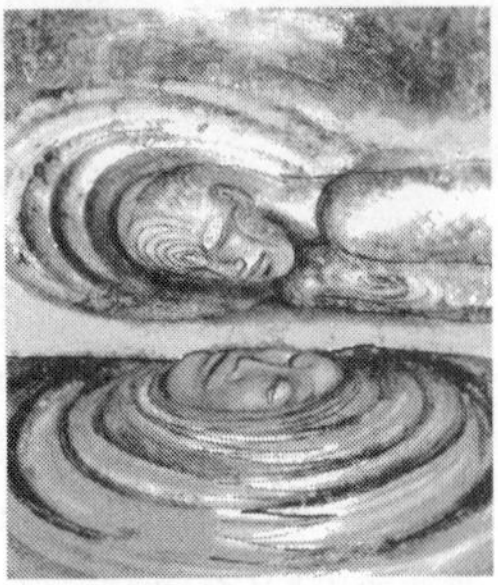

© *Deborah Koff-Chapin 2001*

───── ♂♂♂ Dienstag ─────

♈
♉

Tuesday
27

☽✶♅	9:32 am	
☽✶♄	11:05 am	
☽△♂	2:18 pm	v/c
☽→♉	4:31 pm	

───── ☿☿☿ Mittwoch ─────

♉

Wednesday
28

☉△☽	2:29 am
☽□♃	4:13 am
☽□♆	10:31 am

───── ♃♃♃ Donnerstag ─────

♉

Thursday
29

♂→♍	7:38 am	
☿□♃	12:21 pm	
☽□♅	9:44 pm	v/c

───── ♀♀♀ Freitag ─────

♉
♊

Friday
30

☽→♊	4:45 am	
☽□♂	5:55 am	
☽△♉	1:20 pm	
☽✶♃	5:07 pm	
☉□☽	7:31 pm	
☽△♆	10:03 pm	

Waning Half Moon in ♊ Gemini 7:31 pm PDT

All aspects in Pacific Daylight Time; add 3 hours for EDT; add 7 hours for GMT

Reinvention

I went on an all women's raft trip through Westwater Canyon on the Colorado River. For a week I heeded the house-sized waves on the river and red cliffs where cougars perched to watch rafters below. There was a wisp of a woman in the flotilla. Physically she looked like the winds that ripped through the canyon could carry her to the mountains beyond. Her name is Sarah and this is what she said to me:

"Anybody can reinvent herself at anytime. When I was fifty, I left a marriage of twenty-six years, left a job of twenty, to go to Montana and teach school on the Crow Reservation. I moved there and realized it was the first time I laughed in twenty-six years."

Sarah looked so calm, so unstressed, so young at fifty-two. Back home I commuted three hours a day to a job that kept me awake at night, driving across flat brown land into traffic, urban sprawl and air pollution. I was killing myself for a job that didn't even give me health insurance.

In the canyon I stayed onboard when a giant hydraulic swept half of the crew into the rapids. I awoke one morning to discover mountain lion tracks all around me in the sand. I managed to paddle myself past a storm that took me two strokes back for every stroke I took forward. And I knew when I came home I'd be called crazy by the people around me. I'm not crazy. I'm reinventing myself. I took up kayaking at age forty-six. The boats are stronger than they look, much like a woman I met on the river. They can take you through white water, past lions in the cliffs. I painted the name "Sarah" on the bow of my orange kayak.

□ *Linda "Bucky" Marshall 2001*

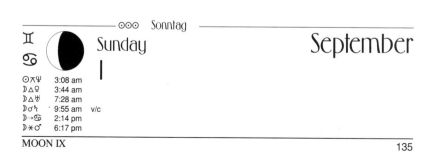

ħħħ Samstag

♊

Saturday
31

☽☌♀ 9:47 am

⊙⊙⊙ Sonntag

♊
♋

Sunday
1

September

⊙⊼♆ 3:08 am
☽△♀ 3:44 am
☽△♅ 7:28 am
☽☌ħ 9:55 am v/c
☽→♋ 2:14 pm
☽✶♂ 6:17 pm

September

Kepakemapa

♋

Monday
2

☿⚹♃ 12:53 am
☽□☿ 2:47 am
☉⚹☽ 8:29 am

African Queen
© Kit Skeoch 2000

♂♂♂ Pōʻalua

♋
♌

Tuesday
3

♀△♅ 8:40 am
♂△♇ 9:29 am
☽□♀ 1:31 pm   v/c
☽→♌ 7:36 pm

☿☿☿ Pōʻakolu

♌

Wednesday
4

☽♂♃ 7:52 am
☿△♆ 7:54 am
☽☍♆ 10:23 am
☽⚹♅ 10:32 am
☽△♇ 8:41 pm

♃♃♃ Pōʻahā

♌
♍

Thursday
5

♀△♄ 7:26 am
☽☍♅ 3:07 pm
☽⚹♄ 5:58 pm
☽⚹♀ 6:33 pm   v/c
☽→♍ 9:16 pm

♀♀♀ Pōʻalima

♍

Friday
6

☽♂♂ 5:20 am
☉♂☽ 8:10 am
☽□♀ 9:07 pm
♇sD 9:40 pm

New Moon in ♍ Virgo 8:10 pm PDT

All aspects in Pacific Daylight Time; add 3 hours for EDT; add 7 hours for GMT

A Tribute

"A Tribute" was written in 1993 and celebrates the first twenty years of Sweet Honey in The Rock.

Twenty years!/Twenty-one women in song/Waging battle with the knowledge/That the struggle is long/From 1973 to '93 and beyond/ Twenty years and twenty-one women/With support so strong/ Move from continent to continent/Singing our songs/Fighting "isms" from a system/Pitting right against wrong/African Queens conscious of our past/With integrity and pride that/Will always last/ Never forgetting the examples/Of those who died/Sacrificing their lives for us to survive/They fought injustice/From slavery to apartheid/To build a world based on truth . . . /No more lies!

Chorus: Rock! The Rock! In The Rock!
               Honey In The Rock!
               Sweet Honey In The Rock!

Just think about the richness of a land/Where honey flows from the rocks;/Imagine, if you can/The strength of a rock,/The sweetness of honey/So much like a woman it ain't even funny/Try to crack a rock and you will find/Like the power of a woman/It'll blow your mind/ Taste a little honey and you will see/It was just what you were missing;/Just what you need/Sweet Honey In The Rock!

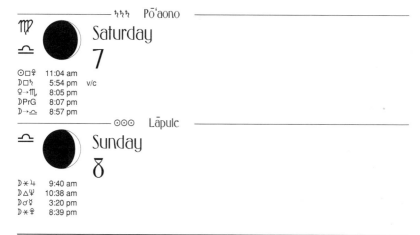

ꜛꜛꜛ   Pōʻaono

♍︎
♎︎
Saturday
7

⊙□♀	11:04 am	
☽□♄	5:54 pm	v/c
♀→♏︎	8:05 pm	
☽PrG	8:07 pm	
☽→♎︎	8:57 pm	

⊙⊙⊙   Lāpule

♎︎
Sunday
☉

☽✷♃	9:40 am
☽△♆	10:38 am
☽♂♉	3:20 pm
☽✷♀	8:39 pm

Grandmother Cedar, Grandmother Pine

She has faced the ax. She has been leveled for cornfields.
The golf course is her deathbed. She has been chopped down,
piled end to end in choking rivers, split, stacked, nailed, pounded and
burned for fuel, burned for heat, burned by the careless cigarette.
Her body made the rugged piers, made the ships
which were loaded down with tea, cotton, sugar, cotton, men.
She made the wealthy, made the wheel, made the wagons
as the wild was beat back against the mountains.
And still she persists in being
despite lightning, mud slides, chainsaws,
the sprawling growth of the city crippling her limbs.

I hide inside my home wearing her body like a box
to protect me from the cold, prying eyes of strangers.
She stares back at me from these walls
fixing me to the map of wives with my lemon-stained rag.
I bury my sweaters in her chest to keep them from the gnawing moths;
I dance across her spine pointing my toes and leaping
to give form to my howling pleasure—
and in the gesture of the hopeful, I bundle up the roots of a small one,
dig a hole, soak it, place the sapling into the mud,
its sweet spicy branches brushing against my sweat.

Remember the trees who make this life possible,
who some call grandmother,
because they, like us, have parents, ancestors, live in community.
I have seen them dancing in their ceremony of bending low
when the wind rushes in from the north.
Trees are made from all things holy:
rain, soil, sunlight, bogs, bees, and centuries—
do I honor them properly
when I put another log on the fire,
when I decorate holiday branches with tinsel,
when I pick my teeth with a toothpick
when I jot down notes for a meeting?
Even this page which you hold in your hands as you read
is made from their lips
giving my voice a place to rest or rise up keening—

X. GRIEVE/PROTECT

Moon X: September 6–October 6

New Moon in ♍ Virgo: Sep. 6; Full Moon in ♓ Pisces: Sep. 21; Sun in ♎ Libra: Sep. 22

Redwood Magic
© *Lilian de Mello 1998*

September
Septembro

───── ☽☽☽ lundo ─────

♎︎
♏︎

Monday
9

☽△♅ 2:25 pm
☽△♄ 5:52 pm v/c
☽→♏︎ 8:48 pm
☽♂♀ 11:34 pm

───── ♂♂♂ mardo ─────

♏︎

Tuesday
10

☽⚹♂ 9:20 am
☽□♃ 10:35 am
☽□♆ 10:51 am

───── ☿☿☿ merkredo ─────

♏︎
♐︎

Wednesday
11

☉⚹☽ 3:17 am
♃☍♆ 5:07 am
☽□♅ 3:52 am v/c
♂⚹♆ 7:19 pm
☽→♐︎ 10:44 pm
♀⚹♄ 11:59 pm

───── ♃♃♃ ĵaŭdo ─────

♐︎

Thursday
12

☽⚹♆ 1:33 pm
☽△♃ 2:04 pm
☽□♂ 2:28 pm
☽⚹☿ 9:31 pm

───── ♀♀♀ vendredo ─────

♐︎

Friday
13

☽♂♀ 12:50 am
☉□☽ 11:08 am
☽⚹♅ 8:20 pm

□ *Genet Rose Kemp 2001*

I Am Infinite

Waxing Half Moon in ♐︎ Sagittarius 11:08 am PDT

All aspects in Pacific Daylight Time; add 3 hours for EDT; add 7 hours for GMT

Timber Sales

Lost & Saved

An amazing set of coincidences saved the forest in the Cobble Creek timber sale area.

650 Year-old tree, Paw Timber Sale, Umpqua National Forest

A group of forest activists I was a part of discovered BLM (Bureau of Land Management) cutting a few old trees illegally. We stopped them and reported them to other agencies. Soon afterward, I went for a hike in the area with my friend Abbey, a lichenologist. She found a very, very rare lichen on the downed old trees—a lichen which usually grows *only* in the very tops of trees over 400 years old and only at relatively low elevations. No one would ever have known about it, if those few old trees hadn't been cut and if Abbey and I hadn't happened to go for a hike to the right place. Abbey informed BLM of her discovery and BLM has not been able to find a way around the law forbidding them to destroy this lichen site.

See Resources, page 188   *photo and writing ¤ Francis Eatherington 2000*

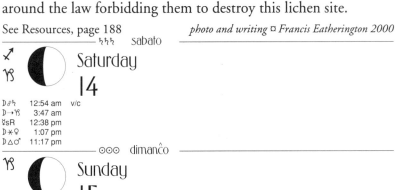

♐
♑

Saturday 14

sabato

☽☍♄	12:54 am	v/c
☽→♑	3:47 am	
☿sR	12:38 pm	
☽⚹♀	1:07 pm	
☽△♂	11:17 pm	

♑

Sunday 15

dimanĉo

☽□♅	4:11 am	
☉△☽	10:58 pm	v/c

September
Septemba

───── ☽☽☽ Jumatatu ─────

Her Loss is Her Gain
© Kathleen Gaitt 1989

♑

Monday
♒
16

☽→♒   11:54 am

───── ♂♂♂ Jumanne ─────

♒

Tuesday
17

☽□♀   12:59 am
☽☌♆   4:14 am
☽☍♃   6:40 am
☽△♅   12:30 pm
☽⚹♀   4:57 pm

───── ☿☿☿ Jumatano ─────

♒

Wednesday
♓
18

☉⛎♅   1:14 pm
☽☌♅   1:54 pm
☽△♄   7:35 pm   v/c
☽→♓   10:18 pm

───── ♃♃♃ Alhamisi ─────

♓
Thursday
19

♀□♆   2:19 pm
☽△♀   3:04 pm

───── ♀♀♀ Ijumaa ─────

♓
Friday
20

☽☍♂   1:47 am
☽□♀   4:14 am

───────────────────────────────

All aspects in Pacific Daylight Time; add 3 hours for EDT; add 7 hours for GMT

Year at a Glance for ♎ LIBRA (Sept. 22–Oct. 23)

An inspired call to action that involved travel or education in 2001, could be the catalyst for a developmental leap in your work in 2002. You may shift from student to teacher, perhaps in frustration with the compromises or oppressiveness of educational systems. Remember—learning is finding out what you already know. Teaching is letting others know they know it as well as you do.

If you have young children, their giftedness, sensitivity and their rebelliousness become more pronounced. The challenge here is to continually adjust the balance between allowing them greater autonomy and providing safe limits. You won't be able to protect them from some of the pain of being human.

Eros inspires you and electrifies all areas of your life. Whatever makes you feel alive, do it. If you feel truly juicy in even one creative arena, all of your life will flow more smoothly. The constraints of words drive you to experiment with the more fluid imagery of art or music. Libra, this is a highly creative time in your life. The skills of a mentor or coach could fine tune your gifts. Sudden or unusual romantic involvements in the last few years feed the wild spirit in you and remind you of the necessity for play. Existing relationships must step out of their frames or they will wither.

How to do this? Welcome mystery, unknowing and the need to become stronger as individuals. Rewrite your futures together. What Libra is about is discovering and inventing new possible forms of relationship. Share what you discover. In this area you are innovator and pioneer.

© *Gretchen Lawlor 2001*

© *Deborah Koff-Chapin 2001*

ℏℏℏ Jumamosi

♓
♈ ○ Saturday 21

☉☌☽	6:59 am	
☽□♄	7:36 am	v/c
☽→♈	10:11 am	
☿⚹♃	11:44 am	
☉□♄	2:47 pm	

Full Moon in ♓ Pisces 6:59 am PDT

☉☉☉ Jumapili

♈ ○ Sunday 22

♂□♀	1:09 am	☽△♀	4:42 pm
☽⚹♆	3:09 am	☽ApG	8:27 pm
☽☌♅	6:08 am	☉→♎	9:55 pm
☽△♃	7:43 am		

Equinox

♎

Sun in Libra 9:55 pm PDT

Weaving a Web of Solidarity

This is a call for feminist action against corporate globalization and the Free Trade Agreement of the Americas (FTAA). We become spiders, spinning a new web of connection out of our rage, our love. We weave together our hopes and dreams, our aspirations, our indictments, our testimony, our visions. We write on ribbons, strips of cloth, rags. We draw, paint, knot cords, braid yarn, whisper into pieces of string. From these materials we weave our web to resist the web of corporate control. If they ignore our voices, the cries of women will haunt them and undo all their plans. Though they erect a fence to stop us, we twine our web through its mesh to be the visible symbol of the power of women and the revolution we weave. When they try to wall us out of their meetings, they only wall themselves in. We claim all of the world beyond their wall.

□ *excerpted and reprinted from anti-FTAA flyer for action in Quebec City, 2001*

Five Reasons to Oppose the FTAA

Earth: The FTAA would allow corporations to sue governments that attempt to ban genetically engineered crops, regulate unsafe foods, ban pesticides or chemicals, protect natural resources, regulate logging or enforce safety standards.

Air: As the hole in the ozone layer grows, governments would lose the ability to regulate ozone destroying chemicals or to prod corporations to produce technologies that would replace gasoline with renewable, clean alternatives.

Fire: The U.N. now estimates global warming is progressing much faster than anticipated, that the earth's temperature may rise by ten degrees. The FTAA would undermine efforts to control greenhouse emissions or shift to alternative technologies.

Water: The FTAA would allow corporations to control the water resources and hydroelectric resources of the hemisphere. It would undercut attempts to protect water quality and fair water usage and to preserve endangered species.

Community: The FTAA would encourage privatization of schools, universities, medical care, hospitals, libraries, museums, prisons, utilities, transportation, broadcasting and many other services previously provided or regulated by communities and governments.

See Resources, page 188.   *excerpt © Starhawk 2001*

© *Julianne Skai Arbor 2000*

Fall Equinox

This is the harvest time. Green turns to gold, a subtle stillness is in the air that whispers of cold to come. This is the time when plants ripen fruit, mature seed and prepare to die or turn inwards. For us it is a time to prepare and harvest nourishing foods and herbs that will see us through the winter months. Fruits such as elderberries and rosehips (vitamin C), tubers such as sunchokes (balances blood sugar) or seeds of burdock and thistles (cleanses the liver) are all harvested, dried and stored for the winter. Once the leaves start to fall and nights are cold you can harvest bark off trees. Cutting parallel with the trunk of the tree, prune off branches 1/2"–2" wide, then strip the bark off these branches with a knife. Never randomly remove bark from the trunk of a living tree. Bark is usually dried for use.

Fruits, seeds and bark are often more difficult to dry as there is more danger of mold. A steady even heat source is good. Health focus for this time of year should be on building up for winter and adjusting any imbalances you have developed over the year. This cycle is fulfilled by the harvest queen or priestess who embodies knowledge and completion.
© *Colette Gardiner 1993, reprinted from* We'Moon '94

September

September

—————))) Montag —————————————

♈
♉

Monday
23

☽⚹♅	1:56 pm	
☽⚹♄	8:29 pm	v/c
☿△♆	8:45 pm	
☽→♉	10:54 pm	

————— ♂♂♂ Dienstag —————————————

♉

Tuesday
24

♀□♃	12:53 am
☽□♆	3:53 pm
☽□♃	9:28 pm
☽☍♀	10:04 pm

————— ☿☿☿ Mittwoch —————————————

♉

Wednesday
25

☿PrG	7:19 am
☽△♂	9:48 am

————— ♃♃♃ Donnerstag —————————————

♉
♊

Thursday
26

☽□♅	2:27 am	v/c
☉□♇	11:14 am	
☽→♊	11:26 am	
☉△☽	7:00 pm	
☽△☿	9:38 pm	

————— ♀♀♀ Freitag —————————————

♊

Friday
27

☽△♆	4:00 am
☽⚹♃	10:22 am
☉♂☿	11:31 am
☽☍♇	5:28 pm

All aspects in Pacific Daylight Time; add 3 hours for EDT; add 7 hours for GMT

SPHere
(Sustainable Peace Here)

*Huge virgin forests were cut to accommodate resettlement resulting from the U.S.-sponsored malarial eradication program and subsequent Nepalese land reform.

excerpt and photos © Huldah Warren 2000
See Resources, page 188.

As women go in search of wood for fuel, the echo of Nepal's depleted forests* rumbles through centuries of empty stomachs fed with their fires. Greens are wildcrafted for *dhalbhat*, the morning meal of rice, lentils and vegetables. Often walking for miles, women return to chop wood for the fire. Soon, the rice that has been planted, harvested, pounded and sifted by women bubbles on the crackling fire . . . For the last five years, I have been living in Nepalese villages as field advisor for SPHere (Sustainable Peace Here), working with Women's Groups, Literacy Classes, Credit Programs, Leadership Training, and Healthy Kid's Classes. These projects are helping women to find their voices in an overpopulated region where they have been harnessed to repeated pregnancies by cultural strictures, and where most have never learned to read or write.

ちちち Samstag

♊
♋

Saturday
28

☽□♂	12:42 am	
♀□♃	8:02 am	
☽△♅	1:19 pm	
☽♂♄	8:01 pm	v/c
☽→♋	10:01 pm	

☉☉☉ Sonntag

♋

Sunday
29

☽□♉	3:07 am
☉□☽	10:03 am
☽△♀	11:28 pm

Waning Half Moon in ♋ Cancer 10:03 am PDT

September/October

Kepakemapa/'Okakopa ⟩⟩⟩ Pōʻakahi

  Monday
30

☽⚹♂ 11:59 am v/c

♂♂♂ Pōʻalua

  Tuesday
1

October

☽→♌ 4:58 am
☽⚹☿ 6:08 am
☉△♆ 8:50 am
☽☍♆ 7:25 pm
☉⚹☽ 8:13 pm

☿☿☿ Pōʻakolu

♌ Wednesday
2

☽♂♃ 2:23 am
☿→♍ 2:25 am
☽□♀ 5:47 am
☽△♀ 7:21 am

♃♃♃ Pōʻahā

♌ Thursday
♍ **3**

☽☍♅ 12:10 am
☽⚹♄ 6:16 am v/c
☽→♍ 7:52 am
☿□♄ 4:09 pm

♀♀♀ Pōʻalima

♍ Friday
4

☽⚹♀ 7:57 am
☽□♀ 8:37 am
☽♂♂ 9:15 pm

All aspects in Pacific Daylight Time; add 3 hours for EDT; add 7 hours for GMT

Newbury Madonna

In the winter of 1995–1996 thousands of protestors launched the largest anti-road campaign in England. A protected forest was threatened by plans to build the Newbury Bypass. Courageous protestors built their homes in the trees, braving often violent eviction in order to slow the progress of the bulldozers. The road was eventually built and the ancient forest and its rare ecosystem were destroyed, but the impact of the protest changed road building policy forever.

art and writing © Selina Di Girolamo 2000

──────── ♄♄♄　Pōʻaono ────────

♍
♎

Saturday
5

☽♂☿	5:27 am	
☽□♄	6:22 am	v/c
☽→♎	7:51 am	
☽△♆	8:48 pm	

──────── ☉☉☉　Lāpule ────────

♎

Sunday
6

☉✳♃	3:38 am	☽✳♀	7:56 am
☽✳♃	4:15 am	☿sD	12:26 pm
☉♂☽	4:18 am	☽△♅	11:26 pm
☽PrG	6:19 am		

New Moon in ♎ Libra 4:18 am PDT

For Eva

You were born underwater
surging from me like a wave
into a world between the secret dark ocean of my womb
and the atmosphere of the world without.
Hale-Bopp burned in the deep and windy November sky
as you floated free, face up in the crimson darkness
of the birthing waters, still in your primal element,
weightless, not yet breathing,
glowing, luminous and otherworldly like the comet above you.
Serene, you looked up at me through the water's surface,
your mother in a world you had not yet entered;
the pearly umbilical rope still linking you to my depths,
an iridescent spiral like the core of a whelk,
formed in the sea, something not created
for this world of light and air.
No longer curled in your amniotic sea,
the infinity of water still cradled you, was still all you knew.
So we made it gentle; your incarnation, your transition
from ocean to ether, spirit to body, within to without;
welcoming you with warmth and water
in hushed darkness and firelight,
while a comet blazed above us like some holy star
telling the world of your birth.

XI. MIDWIFE/TRANSITION

Moon XI: October 6–November 4

New Moon in ♎ Libra: Oct. 6; Full Moon in ♈ Aries: Oct. 21; Sun in ♏ Scorpio: Oct. 23

Dawn Unfolding
© *Carrie Gaylord 2001*

Birthing Ways

Birth is natural, normal, safe, let it be! Let us be reborn as a culture! Let us teach our daughters to trust not fear! Let us get to know our bodies, feel the power within them, value our pain!

Midwives: With women since the dawn of creation. Called to service. Free thinkers, guardians, space holders, shape shifters. Persecuted for recognizing and honoring natural rhythms, life spirals. Still struggling to reclaim autonomy as healers. Activists for informed choice and quality women's health care. Challenging legislature locally and nationally. Setting our own standards of care. Influencing contemporary birth culture.

21st Century Midwives: Rekindling ancient arts and traditions, support, trust, listening, birth as a community event, not a medical emergency! Inviting birth back home to living rooms, bedrooms, back yards.

Midwifery: Rising like a Phoenix from our foremothers' ashes. *Back by popular demand!* In the face of corporate medicine, popular media, misinformation. We are here to stay!

© *Carrie Gaylord 2001*

October

Oktobro

─────))) lundo ─────

Monday
7

☽△♄	5:29 am	v/c
☽→♏	6:57 am	
☽□♆	8:02 pm	
♂⚼♅	10:09 pm	

───── ♂♂♂ mardo ─────

Tuesday
8

☽□♃	4:10 am
☽☌♀	7:42 am
☉⚹♀	2:03 pm
☽□♅	11:25 pm

───── ☿☿☿ merkredo ─────

Wednesday
9

☽⚹♂	12:36 am	
☽⚹☿	5:38 am	v/c
☽→♐	7:21 am	
☿□♄	11:32 am	
☽⚹♆	9:05 pm	

───── ♃♃♃ ĵaŭdo ─────

Thursday
10

☽△♃	6:16 am
☽☌♀	9:22 am
♀sR	11:35 am
☉⚹☽	12:35 pm
☿→♎	10:55 pm

───── ♀♀♀ vendredo ─────

Friday
11

☽⚹♅	2:11 am	
☽□♂	6:01 am	
♄sR	6:01 am	
☽☍♄	9:08 am	v/c
☽→♑	10:45 am	
☽□♀	11:28 am	

All aspects in Pacific Daylight Time; add 3 hours for EDT; add 7 hours for GMT

Solstice/Fire

Solstice* sits in the sweat lodge. Her purification is in progress. She is becoming distilled, potent in her passing—her spirit still evolving, loving us. Butterflies swoop by. Hummingbirds zoom past our heads. The wind caresses our bodies, gently cooling us while across

Solstice
© Amy Schutzer 1998

the mountain ridges another wildfire burns out of control consuming thousands of acres of trees, countless animals and nameless sacred altars. We wait for death here in our green valley, our cottonwood glen, harboring our family pack soon to be one less. We wait for the flames of our own wildfire to pass knowing we can only give love, compassion, kindness in the face of this cycle of life into death into life.

© Eaglehawk 2000

*Solstice was our dog dying of lung cancer on women's land in New Mexico while wildfires were burning all around, including Los Alamos Nuclear Labs (30 miles to the west) and the Pecos National Wilderness (50 miles to the east).

♄♄♄   sabato

♑

Saturday
12

☽⚹♀   2:48 pm
☉□☽   10:33 pm

☉☉☉   dimanĉo   Waxing Half Moon in ♑ Capricorn 10:33 pm PDT

♑
≈

Sunday
13

☽△♂   3:42 pm   v/c
☽→≈   5:51 pm
☽△♅   11:10 pm
♂□♄   11:56 pm

October

Oktoba

☽☽☽ Jumatatu

♒

Monday

14

☽☌♆ 9:31 am
☽☍♃ 9:19 pm
☽□♀ 11:04 pm
☽✶♇ 11:45 pm

♂♂♂ Jumanne

♒

Tuesday

15

☿□⚷ 4:32 am
♂→♎ 10:38 am
☉△☽ 12:54 pm
☽☌♅ 6:21 pm

☿☿☿ Jumatano

♒
♓

Wednesday

16

☽△♄ 2:15 am v/c
☽→♓ 4:07 am

♃♃♃ Alhamisi

♓

Thursday

17

☽△♀ 9:20 am
♀□♃ 9:34 am
☽□♇ 11:17 am

♀♀♀ Ijumaa

♓
♈

Friday

18

☿△♆ 3:46 am
☉△♅ 7:08 am
☽□♄ 2:16 pm v/c
☽→♈ 4:13 pm
☽☍♂ 8:38 pm

All aspects in Pacific Daylight Time; add 3 hours for EDT ; add 7 hours for GMT

Women's Rites/ Women's Mysteries

Lauren's Menarche Ceremony
© Gail K. Nyoka 2000

Ritual practices are at the heart of the women's spirituality movement. Creating and participating in ritual brings value to the passages of our lives, whether they are physical crossroads or emotional transitions. It is through women's rites that we connect to and honor the deepest parts of ourselves, bringing inner knowledge to conscious awareness. Within ritual, we witness and support one another in our paths of healing and our diverse celebrations of the rites of life.

Dianic feminist Goddess-inspired spiritual practice focuses on women's Mysteries, including the five blood mysteries that reflect women's ability to create life, sustain life and return our bodies to the Source in death. Women's rituals also celebrate the earth's seasonal cycles of birth, death and regeneration, and its connection to women's cyclical nature.

When life passages are clearly marked through ritual, we can connect the dots of events in our lives to see the pattern in what may have previously felt like a random series of events. The purpose of ritual is transformation. Given a flexible form, ritual allows room to breathe and incorporates the unforeseen.

© Ruth Barrett 2000, excerpted from
Women's Rites, Women's Mysteries: Creating Personal and Group Ritual

———————————— ♄♄♄ Jumamosi ————————————

♈ ☽ Saturday
19

☽⚹♆	8:48 am
☽☍☿	12:55 pm
☽ApG	9:43 pm
☽△♃	10:33 pm
☽△♀	11:59 pm

———————————— ☉☉☉ Jumapili ————————————

♈ ☽ Sunday
20

♆sD	6:53 am
☽⚹♅	6:48 pm

October
Oktober

𝄞𝄞𝄞 Montag

♈
♉

Monday
21

☉☌☽	12:20 am	
☽⚹♄	2:55 am	v/c
☽→♉	4:57 am	
☽□♆	9:30 pm	

□ *Donna Campbell 1999*

Big

Full Moon in ♈ Aries 12:20 am PDT

♂♂♂ Dienstag

♉

Tuesday
22

☉△♄	6:31 am
☽☍♀	6:53 am
☽□♃	11:51 am
♂□☋	5:13 pm
☿⚹♃	7:20 am

☿☿☿ Mittwoch

♉
♊

Wednesday
23

☿⚹♀	1:49 am	
☽□♅	7:14 am	v/c
☉→♏	7:18 am	
☽→♊	5:17 pm	

♏

Sun in Scorpio 7:18 am PDT

♃♃♃ Donnerstag

♊

Thursday
24

| ☽△♂ | 4:23 am |
| ☽△♆ | 9:35 am |

♀♀♀ Freitag

♊

Friday
25

☽⚹♃	12:11 am
☽☍♀	12:38 am
☽△☿	7:43 am
☽△♅	6:24 pm

All aspects in Pacific Daylight Time; add 3 hours for EST; add 8 hours for GMT

Year at a Glance for ♏ SCORPIO (Oct. 23–Nov. 21)

In 2002, watch for interest from influential people regarding a special skill or resource you possess. In order to maximize this opportunity, you need some additional information. Don't assume you know everything; add perspective and knowledge through travel, specific teachings or legal advice (particularly before August). A crisis regarding joint resources or a change in the circumstances of a beloved may be throwing you into a fresh re-appraisal of life priorities. What is ultimately most important in your life? Be especially aware of the impact of intimate alliances upon your future.

A continuing feeling of restlessness may provoke a physical relocation, though the longing for paradise on earth may keep you in an unsettled state. If you move, you will ultimately appreciate that change was needed to bring out qualities in yourself that would have otherwise remained undeveloped. If you stay put, remember that your home and family dynamics need to be reorganized. Your most steady sense of belonging is likely to come not from a place but from your connection to a quirky and rebellious tribe of souls who share common spiritual ideals. Be open to inspirations from foreign cultures, the lifestyles of another country may most closely fit an emerging need in you to create new community.

Elements of your life which have previously provided stability and definition have been fading away; you surprise even yourself with the radical impulses exploding out of you. Periodically take time out of your busy circumstances for reverie and revision, in order that you may continue to align your plans with your highest spiritual and creative potential. A retreat in September could be profoundly inspiring.

© *Gretchen Lawlor 2001*

Facing Fear
□ *Frankie Hansbearry 1998*

──────── ♄♄♄ Samstag ────────

♊
♋

Saturday
26

☽ ♂ ♄   2:01 am   v/c
☽ → ♋   4:10 am
☉ △ ☽   10:08 am
☽ □ ♂   5:58 pm

──────── ☉☉☉ Sonntag ────────

♋

Sunday
27

☽ △ ♀   12:00 am
♃ △ ♀   3:41 pm

Daylight Savings Time ends 2:00 am PDT

October/November

'Okakopa/Nowemapa))) Pōʻakahi

♋
♌

Monday
28

☽□☿	12:22 am	v/c
♂△♆	6:28 am	
☉✶⚷	6:33 am	
☽→♌	11:20 am	
☿△♅	1:43 pm	
☉□☽	9:28 pm	

Apples bleed
    cider under pressure
Pumpkin entrails
    slime priestess fingers
Turning Death
    to Celebration.
excerpt ¤ Gaia Sophia Hawkin 1998

Waning Half Moon in ♌ Leo 9:28 pm PST

♂♂♂ Pōʻalua

♌

Tuesday
29

☽☍♆	2:07 am
☽✶♂	3:05 am
☽□♀	3:42 am
☽△♀	3:50 pm
☽♂♃	4:06 pm

☿☿☿ Pōʻakolu

♌
♍

Wednesday
30

☽☍♅	7:19 am	
☽✶♀	12:57 pm	
☽✶♄	1:51 pm	v/c
♀□♆	2:53 pm	
☽→♍	3:59 pm	
☿△♄	8:28 pm	

♃♃♃ Pōʻahā

♍

Thursday
31

☉♂♀	4:06 am
☽✶♀	5:13 am
☉✶☽	5:21 am
☉□♆	12:16 pm
☿→♏	2:43 pm
☽□♀	6:47 pm

Samhain/Hallowmas

♀♀♀ Pōʻalima

♍
♎

Friday
1

♀PrG	12:13 am	
☽□♄	3:19 pm	v/c
☽→♎	5:28 pm	

November

All aspects in Pacific Standard Time; add 3 hours for EST; add 8 hours for GMT

Cerridwen

© *Hrana Janto 1993*

Samhain/Hecate/Hallowe'en

Hecate's day is widely considered the most powerful time of the year. The Crone indeed has come into her own as we observe the onset of wintry weather. Until Spring Equinox, Persephone will reside with Hecate in the underworld, learning the mysteries and powers of the deep self. She experiences her solo magic, her eternal soul, her abilities to create and un-create, or heal. This is a good time for divination, communicating with the dead, strong dream teachings, and banishments of all kinds. The veil between the worlds of life and death is thin and the powers of the dark are available to us. Some consider Hallowmas the New Year, the end and beginning of the Goddess' cycle. In olden times witches would hold their greatest gatherings to honor Hecate, sometimes called the "Queen of the Witches."   © *Shekhinah Mountainwater 1991, reprinted from*
We'Moon '98, *excerpted from* Adriadne's Thread (*Crossing Press*)

Sweet Life, Sweet Basilica

Kneeling on the wooden floor in the evening sun, drinking tea,
my fingers caress the roughness of the pottery bowl,
absorbed by my small plants, my chou chou basilica,
marvel at their growing from seed, attentive to their comfort
out in the sunshine, in when it's too cold, just enough water.

I am filled with death, sipping tea, back from hospital,
the sight of her soft dark eyes, skin and bones no hope now,
only a few days to go, so much courage and peace.
My thumb and forefinger fit around her ankle,
I massage her feet with sweet smelling oil,
sensing many light beings around her bed.
Thirty-three years young and not yet old,
she's not afraid of dying, only of pain, of how.
She has lived nine years knowing death would come.

From the eighth floor window we see the whole city
stretching our arms can almost touch the clouds
the swallows swooping and diving.
They come every year, the basil seeds grow again,
and she will not die, she will not die,
we hold hands in silence and fall into softness,
she will pass into the stream, slipping from her body
and explode she says at the heart into the oneness.
My green basilica is a miracle, sweet green life,
the golden stream dressed in white
her ashes scattered at sea, she will come back
to bring her wisdom to the world
to share the love and deep knowing
that has burned through out of suffering.

Rubbing a small leaf on my hands
the scent of basil is strong life, sweet life joy.
A bright pink rose on her white nightdress
a crystal in her hands, accepting, she knows
her feet will not touch the earth this summer.

Matriarchal Grave
© *Puma Lichtblau 1994*

November

 ♄♄♄ Pō'aono

♎ Saturday

2

☽△♆	6:41 am	
☽♂♂	11:57 am	
☽⚹♀	7:12 pm	
☽⚹♃	7:54 pm	

☉☉☉ Lāpule

 ♎
♏ Sunday

3

☽△♅	9:07 am		☿⚹♇	9:38 pm
☽△♄	2:56 pm	v/c	♅sD	10:27 pm
☽PrG	4:32 pm		☿♂♀	11:43 pm
☽→♏	5:10 pm			

Metamorphosis

I saved your life.
I raised you from an egg
smaller than a drop of water.
I fed you leaves of milk,
the only food you know.

Now you are nearly finished
with your tiny body, still smaller
than my smallest finger.
I watch you climbing, searching,
touching for the first time a world
beyond the leaf.

I am so moved by your life.
I watch you.
With my enormous brain
and opposable thumbs
and amazing intellect
I can teach you nothing.

Do you know the beauty
contained within you?
Miraculous wings will take shape
and lead you to nectar.
And you do what you must do
without fear of flight or change.

I offer a prayer for you.
But even this is too rational
and lacks humility.
Finally I ask:
May I be wise, may I be wild enough
to call you teacher.

XII. ALLY/COMMUNE

Moon XII: November 4–December 3

New Moon in ♏ Scorpio: Nov. 4; Full Moon in ♉ Taurus: Nov. 19; Sun in ♐ Sagittarius: Nov. 22

Butterfly Womyn
¤ *Nadine C. Butterfield 2000*

November

Novembro

My aunt kept a bucket with a stick in it under the rain gutter. The stick is for any critters who may have fallen in, so they can crawl back out.

excerpt ¤ Sara-Lou Klein 2000

——))) lundo ——

♏ Monday

4

☽☌♀	1:57 am
☽☌☿	2:19 am
♀⚹⚷	4:46 am
☽□♆	6:14 am
☉☌☽	12:34 pm
☽□♃	7:43 pm

Lunar Samhain
New Moon in ♏ Scorpio 12:34 pm PST

—— ♂♂♂ mardo ——

♏ ♐ Tuesday

5

☽□♅	8:48 am	v/c
☿□♆	2:37 pm	
☽→♐	5:01 pm	

—— ☿☿☿ merkredo ——

♐ Wednesday

6

☽⚹♆	6:31 am
☽⚹♂	4:21 pm
☽☌♀	7:42 pm
☽△♃	8:50 pm

—— ♃♃♃ jaŭdo ——

♐ ♑ Thursday

7

☽⚹♅	10:17 am	
☽☍♄	4:14 pm	v/c
☽→♑	6:59 pm	

—— ♀♀♀ vendredo ——

♑ Friday

8

☽⚹♀	12:52 am
☽⚹♉	6:26 pm
☽□♂	10:26 pm

All aspects in Pacific Standard Time; add 3 hours for EST; add 8 hours for GMT

44 Salmon

The scientists snare numbers with charts of statistics
while you squint from the river boat into folds of water
arching and mottled with wind spittle
and deeper into where the numbers school,
upcurrent over the teeth of dams,
unharmed by turbines and the suck of pumps, so they say.
The scientists multiply numbers like fish eggs hatching
spawned by reasons and equations.
What happens when numbers die?
The scientists arrange them in pi and square roots
and declare there is still plenty to go around.
The salmon disappear.

When the scientists suspend their numbers like hooks
do you bite into the belief of longevity,
the river's ability to look out for herself and the salmon?
Or do you cast your line without hesitation,
the river thick with equations, so they say.
What difference will 44 salmon make this year
if next we have 45?
They offer fractions as bait, calculations as hope.
The salmon disappear.

What good will the rivers be if they are empty and sour?
And which scientist will make a salmon
from electricity or a pristine prime number? *excerpt © Amy Schutzer 1994*

ħħħ   sabato

♑ 🌔 Saturday
       9

⊙✶☽   12:22 am   v/c
⊙□♃   9:06 am
♂✶♀   11:52 pm

⊙⊙⊙   dimanĉo

♑ 🌑 Sunday
♒   10

☽→♒   12:27 am
☽□♀   4:55 am
☽♂♆   3:59 pm

November

Novemba ⟩⟩⟩ Jumatatu

 Monday
11

☿□♃	3:09 am
☽✶♀	7:19 am
☽△♂	8:55 am
☽☍♃	8:59 am
☽□☿	9:49 am
♂✶♃	10:22 am
☉□☽	12:52 pm
☽♂♅	11:48 pm

She Dreams Raven

Waxing Half Moon in ♒ Aquarius 12:52 pm PST

─── ♂♂♂ Jumanne

♒
♓

Tuesday
12

☽△♄	6:06 am	v/c
☽→♓	9:42 am	
☽△♀	12:40 pm	

─── ☿☿☿ Jumatano

♓

Wednesday
13

☽□♀	6:25 pm
☉♂♉	8:40 pm

─── ♃♃♃ Alhamisi

♓
♈

Thursday
14

☉△☽	5:29 am	
☽△♉	5:59 am	
☽□♄	5:38 pm	v/c
☽→♈	9:38 pm	

─── ♀♀♀ Ijumaa

♈

Friday
15

☽✶♆	2:37 pm
☿□♅	11:03 pm

Not too Proud to Howl and Dressed to Kill

© Joyce Radtke 2001

♈ ☾ **Saturday**
16

☽ApG	3:30 am
☽△♀	7:13 am
☽△♃	9:16 am
☽☍♂	3:24 pm

♈
♉ ☾ **Sunday**
17

☽⚹♅	12:15 am	☽☍♀	11:01 am
☉□♅	4:34 am	☿ApG	5:50 pm
☽⚹♄	6:06 am v/c	☿⚻♄	6:36 pm
☽→♉	10:23 am		

November
November

☽☽☽ Montag

♉

Monday
18

☽□♆ 3:23 am
☽□♃ 10:01 pm

© Paula Billups 2000

Good Company

♂♂♂ Dienstag

♉
♊

Tuesday
19

☿→♐ 3:29 am
☽□♅ 12:32 pm
☉☍☽ 5:34 pm v/c
☉⊼♄ 9:22 pm
☽→♊ 10:25 pm

Full Moon in ♉ Taurus 5:34 pm PST
Appulse Lunar Eclipse 5:48 pm PST
Eclipse visible from the Americas, Africa, Europe and Asia Minor

☿☿☿ Mittwoch

♊

Wednesday
20

☽☍☿ 1:14 am
☽△♆ 3:06 pm
♀sD 11:12 pm

♃♃♃ Donnerstag

♊

Thursday
21

☽☍♇ 7:16 am
☽✶♃ 9:22 am
☽△♂ 9:14 pm
☽△♅ 11:18 pm

♀♀♀ Freitag

♊
♋

Friday
22

☉→♐ 3:54 am
☽☌♄ 4:07 am v/c
☽→♋ 8:48 am
☽△♀ 8:58 am

♐

Sun in Sagittarius 3:54 am PST

All aspects in Pacific Standard Time; add 3 hours for EST; add 8 hours for GMT

Year at a Glance for ♐ SAGITTARIUS (Nov. 21–Dec. 21)

A long process of internal work is ending. Now expansion must proceed outwards. Be willing to be more socially active. People want to know what has inspired you from the crises and losses you have experienced in the past few years. In the first half of the year, break an old habit. You are more than ready to move on in so many aspects of your life, this gesture of willingness facilitates more revolutionary shifts. Sudden, unexpected changes turn out to your advantage. Banks want to loan you money, other people's resources are generously shared with you. Intimate encounters touch you deeply.

From August onwards, travel or educational opportunities are particularly inspiring, helping you to connect with a new, more socially or politically influential self. If you are a spiritual explorer, mystical experiences are more commonplace. Your life needs to be a personal example of your principles. However, watch for tendencies towards self-righteousness or excessive pride. Focus your awareness on others around you. What are they in your life for, and why are you in theirs? Your purpose and destiny can only be revealed in relation to others. This year, your one-to-one relationships challenge you to cooperate, to have compassion and understanding. Mutual progress comes from everyone clarifying intentions.

Your communication style continues to be innovative, evocative, with inspired but occasionally muddled thinking. Pay attention to feedback from your chosen audience, be willing to recraft your work. Petty upsets in daily affairs provoke a need for tolerance and a devotion to clarity in your own communications. Continue to uncover and develop those qualities in your personality which amplify your unique style.

© *Gretchen Lawlor 2001*

Prayer Arrow
For "Miracle" the White Buffalo
▫ Joan R. Riise 2001

———— ♄♄♄　Samstag ————

♋ ☽ **Saturday**
23

♂△♅　2:20 pm

———— ☉☉☉　Sonntag ————

♋
♌ ☽ **Sunday**
24

☽□♂　8:51 am　v/c
☿⚹♆　2:38 pm
☽→♌　5:00 pm
☽□♀　5:37 pm
☉△☽　10:06 pm

November
Nowemapa

♌︎

Monday
25

☽☍♆	8:35 am
☽△♅	10:56 am
☽△♀	11:37 pm

———— ♂︎♂︎♂︎   Pōʻalua ——————————

♌︎
♍︎

Tuesday
26

☽♂♃	1:31 am
☽☍♅	2:09 pm
☽✶♂	5:35 pm
☽✶♄	5:51 pm v/c
♂△♄	10:34 pm
☽→♍︎	10:41 pm

———— ☿☿☿   Pōʻakolu ——————————

♍︎

Wednesday
27

☽✶♀	12:02 am
☉□☽	7:46 am
☽□♅	10:22 pm

———— ♃♃♃   Pōʻahā —————————— Waning Half Moon in ♍︎ Virgo 7:46 am PST

♍︎

Thursday
28

☽□♀	4:01 am
☽□♄	9:01 pm v/c

———— ♀♀♀   Pōʻalima ——————————

♍︎
♎︎

Friday
29

☽→♎︎	1:54 am
☉✶☽	2:25 pm
☽△♆	4:17 pm

We Are the World

There is no us and them. There is only us. We—all of us who occupy this planet: organic and inorganic; living and not; past, present, and future—are the world.

We come from the earth and return to her belly. We are made of the same substance as the sea, the soil, the stars. There are, and ever have been, only so many molecules in existence, and all the rest— birth, growth, death, development, change, evolution, species—is really just about recycling.

We breathe the same air as our cave-dwelling ancestors; inhaling and exhaling, exchanging carbon dioxide and oxygen with our plant relatives untold billions of times over the millennia. And the same holds true for water. It rains, it pools, it evaporates. We drink, we pee. Again and again and again in a grand scale cosmic round robin.

All borders and boundaries and separations are pure illusion. Each time we touch someone, we leave some of our skin atoms behind and pick up a parcel of new ones. Thus we merge, literally becoming part of each other. I am you and you are me and we are we.

We are all in this together, inextricably bound on our beautiful blue planet spinning through space. Remember that extraordinary photograph of Earth taken from the moon? We are one team, one community, one world, one living, breathing entity. And the sooner we realize it, the happier, safer and saner we will be.

excerpt ¤ Donna Henes, Urban Shaman 2000

ꜧꜧꜧ   Pōʻaono

♎ **Saturday**

30

☿☌♀	2:50 am	⊙⚹♆	5:38 pm
☽⚹♀	6:11 am	☿△♃	6:19 pm
☽⚹☿	6:34 am	☽△♅	7:28 pm
☽⚹♃	7:48 am	☽△♄	10:15 pm

⊙⊙⊙   Lāpule

♎
♏ **Sunday**

1

December

☽☌♂	3:06 am	v/c
☽→♏	3:15 am	
♂→♏	6:26 am	
☽☌♀	6:38 am	
☽□♆	5:22 pm	

Eastern Oregon

You are the woman and I am your tears.
Let me splash to the ground and freshen
the flowers upon the grave
of each pioneer life struck down too soon.
Let me pour from dark clouds that hold
your grief and cleanse the remains of
Chinese miners who struck hate not gold.
Let me fall in torrents on the gaping earth
where whole villages had no immunities
to the new disease, no hope of escaping death.
Let go of me. Let me be a faint memory
like a tortoise caught midstroke in lava.
Let pain become rock. Make land from the sea.
Make peace from volcanic rage.

You are the hills and I am the river
Let me wash your feet.
Let me run through your deepest ravines.
Tell me your secrets.
Let me kiss away each grain of sand
and frame your stories in time.
In the warmth of the sun
let me uncover the agony of your past
In this new light your awesome scars
will be marks of beauty, beyond contest.
You will stand against an immense sky
barely large enough to hold your spirit.
Your pale-green against the deep-blue will defy
any poet's words, scientist's imagination
or any god's challenge to humble you.
In the end, it's you who will win.
Let me restore your mantle.
Let me close your wounds
so you may reign as a monument
towering over all and mother of this age.

excerpt © Shirley Kishiyama 2001

ARTWORK: **Remembering Grandmother** © Donna Goodwin 2000

XIII. HONOR/EMBRACE

Moon XIII: December 3–January 2

New Moon in ♐ Sagittarius: Dec. 3; Full Moon in ♊ Gemini: Dec. 19; Sun in ♑ Capricorn: Dec. 21

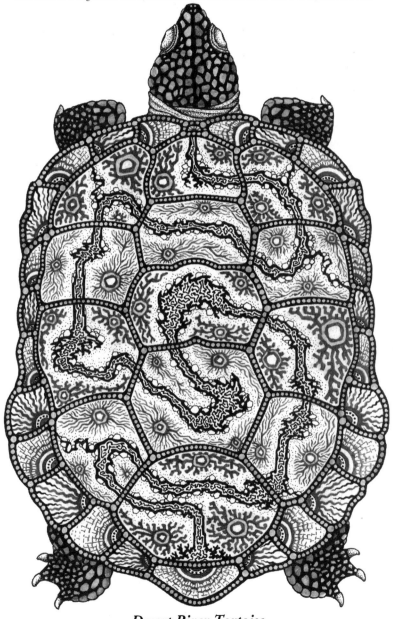

Desert River Tortoise
© *Lorena Babcock Moore 1994*

December

Decembro

♏ Monday

2

☽PrG	12:46 am	
☽□♃	8:37 am	
☽□♅	8:15 pm	v/c

© Donna Goodwin 2000

Remembering Grandmother

♏
♐ Tuesday

3

☽→♐	3:58 am	
☽⚹♆	6:16 pm	
☉☌☽	11:34 pm	

Total Solar Eclipse (2 min., 4 sec.) 11:32 pm PST
Eclipse visible from Africa and Australia
New Moon in ♐ Sagittarius 11:34 pm PST

♐ Wednesday

4

♃sR	4:22 am	
☽☌♀	8:18 am	
☽△♃	9:43 am	
☽☌☿	8:10 pm	
☽⚹♅	9:45 pm	
☽☍♄	11:55 pm	v/c

♐
♑ Thursday

5

☽→♑	5:39 am	
☽⚹♂	10:10 am	
☿⚹♅	11:09 am	
☽⚹♀	12:20 pm	v/c

♑ Friday

6

| ☿☍♄ | 5:36 am |

All aspects in Pacific Standard Time; add 3 hours for EST; add 8 hours for GMT

Transforming Sensitivity:
From Canary to Voice of the Earth

People with multiple chemical sensitivity have often been referred to as "canaries in the mine." This honors us as acting as messengers about the toxicity of our environment. But it doesn't offer a way up and out of the mine. The canary was a disposable indicator, a living scientific instrument. I prefer to think of us as the voice of the earth. Our bodies are part of the larger body of the earth. And since we speak with human voices, we say what our bodies are experiencing. We put into words what other beings in nature are also saying non-verbally. And in speaking, I believe there is great power. When I speak with my speaking/writing voice, I believe I free my body from the burden of speaking only by reacting.

When I first developed chemical sensitivities, a healer suggested this was an initiation into serving the planet by serving the air. I decided this meant that I needed to be part of clearing the air, by teaching about environmentally safer options.

Even when I was declining physically, that purpose kept me alive. Now that I am in an upward healing spiral, I also think about the other aspect of the voice. Singing and working with healing sound have become very important to me in my healing process. Being the voice of the earth can also mean singing about creating better ways of living and celebrating life. I'm not interested in being the canary in the mine; I'd like to be the bird that sings and heals!

© *Deborah Mayaan 2000, adapted from* Environmentally Safer Living *(Three Points Press)*
See Resources, page 188.

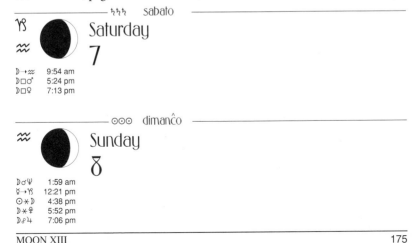

ㅎㅎㅎ sabato

Saturday
7

♑
♒

☽→♒   9:54 am
☽□♂   5:24 pm
☽□♀   7:13 pm

⊙⊙⊙ dimanĉo

Sunday
♉

♒

☽♂♆   1:59 am
♉→♑   12:21 pm
⊙⚹☽   4:38 pm
☽⚹♀   5:52 pm
☽☍♃   7:06 pm

December
Desemba ———————— ☽☽☽ Jumatatu ————————————————

♒︎
♓︎

Monday
9

☉☌♀ 8:55 am
☽☌♅ 9:02 am
☽△♄ 10:35 am v/c
☽→♓︎ 5:46 pm
☽✶♀ 9:52 pm
☉△♃ 11:16 pm

———————— ♂♂♂ Jumanne ————————————————

♓︎

Tuesday
10

☽△♂ 4:53 am
♀ApG 6:07 am
☽△♀ 6:32 am

———————— ☿☿☿ Jumatano ————————————————

♓︎

Wednesday
11

☽☐♀ 4:00 am
☉☐☽ 7:49 am
☽☐♄ 9:02 pm v/c

———————— ♃♃♃ Alhamisi ————————————————   Waxing Half Moon in ♓︎ Pisces 7:49 am PST

♓︎
♈︎

Thursday
12

☽→♈︎ 4:58 am
☽☐♅ 5:54 pm
☽✶♆ 11:06 pm

———————— ♀♀♀ Ijumaa ————————————————

♈︎

Friday
13

☽△♀ 4:35 pm
☽△♃ 5:18 pm
☽ApG 7:51 pm
☿✶♂ 9:25 pm
♀✶♄ 10:01 pm
♀☐♆ 11:18 pm

All aspects in Pacific Standard Time; add 3 hours for EST; add 8 hours for GMT

When the Grandmothers Speak the Earth will be Healed
© *Deborah LeSueur 2001*

--- ♄♄♄ Jumamosi ---

♈
♉

Saturday
14

☉△☽	1:58 am	
☽⚹♅	8:48 am	
☽⚹♄	9:18 am	v/c
☿☌♃	12:11 pm	
☽→♉	5:43 pm	
☿⚹♀	11:09 pm	

--- ☉☉☉ Jumapili ---

♉

Sunday
15

♂□♆	8:08 am	
♂⚹♃	10:58 am	
☽□♆	12:00 pm	
☽☍♂	12:12 pm	
☽☍♀	2:13 pm	
☽△♅	3:18 pm	

December
Dezember

───── ⊃⊃⊃ Montag ─────

♉

Monday
16

☽□♃ 5:40 am
♄△♅ 1:36 pm
☽□♅ 9:11 pm v/c

Midnight Womyn
◻ Nadine C. Butterfield 2000

───── ♂♂♂ Dienstag ─────

♉
♊

Tuesday
17

☽→♊ 5:43 am
♄PrG 5:46 am
☉☍♄ 9:28 am
☉✶♅ 11:50 am
☽△♆ 11:34 pm

───── ☿☿☿ Mittwoch ─────

♊

Wednesday
18

♃△♀ 5:40 am
☽✶♃ 4:14 pm
☽☍♀ 4:18 pm

───── ♃♃♃ Donnerstag ─────

♊
♋

Thursday
19

☽♂♄ 6:53 am
☽△♅ 7:30 am
☉☍☽ 11:10 am v/c
☽→♋ 3:30 pm

───── ♀♀♀ Freitag ─────

Full Moon in ♊ Gemini 11:10 am PST

♋

Friday
20

♉⊼♃ 1:58 pm
☽△♂ 2:43 pm
☽△♀ 5:46 pm

───────────────────

All aspects in Pacific Standard Time; add 3 hours for EST; add 8 hours for GMT

Year at a Glance for ♑ CAPRICORN (Dec. 21–Jan. 20)

Acutely aware of detail in 2002, Capricorn subjects self and others to meticulous scrutiny. What excesses could you temper, particularly in health habits? In your work environment, where could you introduce more efficient techniques or routines? You are most effective this year when you focus upon practical, concrete matters. You may feel driven to put your affairs in order, anticipating a significant change in your work within the next year.

Be willing to act upon hunches regarding financial advantage, especially if they involve issues or products on the cutting edge of popular tastes. Be imaginative in ways to generate income. You may need to borrow money to implement a dream, especially in the latter part of the year. People are willing to help you out, but don't allow yourself to take on more debt than you will need just because it's being offered.

You continue to experience unforseen income fluctuations, though this phase is nearly over (ends 2003). Any big change occuring this year will make your life richer and more rewarding in the long run. Insight into an unresolvable problem allows you to drop the weight of responsibility from your own shoulders.

Your intangible gifts and talents become more obvious; others are inspired by your imagination, your faith, your devotion. Your interests lean towards unraveling mysteries and spiritual concerns.

An auspicious alliance may be offered between mid-2001 and mid-2002, either personal or professional. If you are not already involved, here comes more life! This could be a long lasting association. In an established relationship, expand your horizons together—travel or study something together. Be generous towards each other. Your social life improves, so does your capacity for intimacy.

© Gretchen Lawlor 2001

♄♄♄   Samstag

♋
♌   Saturday
21

☽⚺♅   1:31 am   v/c
☉→♑   5:14 pm
☽→♌   10:48 pm

☉☉☉   Sonntag

♌   Sunday
22

☽⚺♆   3:27 pm
☽□♂   11:51 pm

Solstice

Sun in Capricorn 5:14 pm PST

♑

Winter Solstice

Winter Solstice Ritual. A huge labyrinth created out of boughs; fir, basalm, pine and cedar that we have collected as we trudged through thigh-deep snow. Sweet soothing smells. Cleansing. A small cedar circle in the centre, crowned by obsidian, dark as the darkest night, and a fistful of bright red mountain ash berries, an offering to the Goddess. Stone containers are placed on the altar, hard as the bare bones of winter, in which to shake seeds from the Acoma seed pot. Ink black paper boxes inscribed with silver, holding gifts of the night, are set against the white snow.

We cast a wide circle around the boughs under the light of the half-veiled moon. Running, singing, laughing; her magic overtook us. As we each walked the labyrinth the others stood as sentinels, holding the circle, witnessing each other. Silently, we spoke our lives through our bodies as we walked, ran, skipped, trudged, fell to our knees, flew, plodded, collapsed in the snow, twisted and turned on our way to the centre. Each woman's journey resonated inside me, *I am you, you are me, we are all together.* Moonshadows danced on the ice white snow. The crunch of our footsteps echoed in the night, along with the jingle of bells to mark our journey. The moon shone her white light, moving across the sky, as strong as our beating hearts. Wisps of cloud blew away, until at last, the moon, her veils lifted, her face smooth and clear as white ice, illuminated the night.

Only when we had all completed our path to the centre of the labyrinth did we light the centre candle, welcoming the return of the light. We spread a blanket on the snow for a Winter Solstice picnic; a warming feast of Kali and Lemon Ginger tea, popcorn and poppy seed cookies. We gathered up the labyrinth of boughs, leaving the field clean and white under the moon's light. Cold to the bone, we headed to the warmth of our cars, thoughts of soft blankets and comforting beds pulling us homeward.

I awoke early the next morning with images of the labyrinth resonating in my head and heart, images of my sisters on their journey graced by white winter light. Solstice. Darkness. Moon shadows. Seeds in stone boxes. We have honored the night, the white bones of winter.

© *Diane Goldsmith 2001*

The Temple of Sekhmet

□ Monica Sjöö 2001

Located on Highway 95, forty-five miles north of Las Vegas, Nevada and fifteen miles south of the National Nuclear Test Site, a statue of Sekhmet, ancient image of women's power, sits regally inside her temple. She faces the test site to heal Mother Earth. The temple, rising in the middle of the Mojave Desert, was built in honor of Sekhmet, the lion-headed Egyptian goddess of birth, fertility and rage.

This beautiful space serves the peace and spirituality community as a place for gathering, centering and meditation. The sand-colored stucco temple is open to all the elements of nature. In the center of the temple is a sacred fire pit for ceremony. The temple provides a calm space of refuge for opponents of nuclear weapons tests. Peace and reverence live within the temple along with a quiet sense of self-empowerment. A full Wiccan calendar of events honoring the Wheel of the Year is celebrated.

Because the desert is fragile, when you visit it is requested that you look where you walk. Every animal, every plant, every rock and every grain of sand is our spirit.

© Patricia Pearlman and Genevieve Vaughn 2001

See Resources, page 188.

December

Kēkēmapa

♌

Monday
23

☽□♀	3:34 am	
☽♂♃	6:07 am	
☽△♀	6:56 am	
☽⚹♄	7:27 am	
☽☍♅	8:58 pm	v/c

♂♂♂ Pō'alua

♌
♍

Tuesday
24

☽→♍	4:05 am	
☉△☽	8:48 am	
♀□♃	5:26 pm	

☿☿☿ Pō'akolu

♍

Wednesday
25

☽⚹♂	6:56 am	
☽□♀	11:24 am	
☽⚹♀	11:25 am	
☽△☿	9:45 pm	
☽□♄	11:09 pm	v/c

♃♃♃ Pō'ahā

♍
♎

Thursday
26

☽→♎	7:53 am	
☿⚻♄	4:07 pm	
☉□☽	4:31 pm	
☽△♆	11:54 pm	

♀♀♀ Pō'alima

Waning Half Moon in ♎ Libra 4:31 pm PST

♎

Friday
27

☽⚹♃	1:08 pm	
☽⚹♀	2:41 pm	
♂□♃	11:22 pm	

In an era of unprecedented deforestation there can be better ways to honor evergreens (a symbol of life everlasting!) than to kill them . . .

excerpt □ Peggy Sue McRae 1993, reprinted from We'Moon '96

All aspects in Pacific Standard Time; add 3 hours for EST; add 8 hours for GMT

A Call to Earth Healers

Imagine a world where science, technology, politics and economics are guided by a respect for the sacredness of all Life . . . a world where human brain power grapples with the creative challenge of finding ways for large populations to live in balance on Mother Earth. Humans can create marvelous things. Imagine converting to solar power, wind power, organic farming, pollutant-free transportation.

Imagine using our knowledge to help heal Mother Earth. Not only do we need to halt current environmentally degrading practices, we also need to help Mother Earth to recover from injuries that we have inflicted upon her precious and beautiful body. We can help by replenishing depleted soils, planting trees, purifying waters through hydroponic plant systems, creating ponds in strategic places to regenerate biodiversity. And I am sure we can discover many more ways to help . . . although we can never bring back the species that have become extinct.

Come together, Earth Healers, let's join our efforts to make this world the paradise that it was meant to be, for all creatures. Awakened ones, we have a responsibility. The time has come for ACTION. We have been preparing ourselves for this for a long time. Let's go!

◻ *Priestess Maya White Sparks 1999, excerpted from "A Call to Earth Healers" in* Close To Mother Earth *(Flint Hill, USA), Vol. VIII, No. 3, Earth Day/May Eve 1999)*

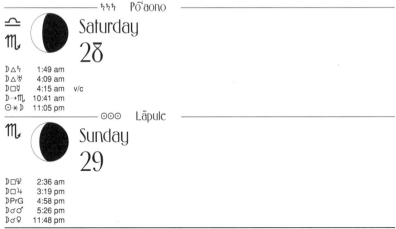

———— ♄♄♄　Pō'aono ————

♎ Saturday
♏ 28

☽△♄	1:49 am	
☽△♅	4:09 am	
☽□♉	4:15 am	v/c
☽→♏	10:41 am	
☉⚹☽	11:05 pm	

———— ☉☉☉　Lāpule ————

♏ Sunday
29

☽□♆	2:36 am
☽□♃	3:19 pm
☽PrG	4:58 pm
☽☌♂	5:26 pm
☽☌♀	11:48 pm

December/January

Decembro/Januaro   ☽☽☽   lundo ────────────────────

♏︎
♐︎   Monday
30

☽□♅   6:39 am
☽✶♉   9:04 am   v/c
☽→♐︎   1:01 pm

──────────────── ♂♂♂   mardo ────────────────────

♐︎   Tuesday
31

☽✶♆   5:04 am
☽△♃   5:26 pm
☽☌♀   7:48 pm

──────────────── ☿☿☿   merkredo ────────────────

♐︎
♑︎   Wednesday   January 2003
1

☽☍♄   6:10 am
☉☌♇   8:02 am
☽✶♅   9:23 am   v/c
♀⊼♄   10:14 am
☽→♑︎   3:42 pm

──────────────── ♃♃♃   ĵaŭdo ────────────────────

♑︎   Thursday
2

☿sR   10:19 am
☉☌☽   12:23 pm

                                    New Moon in ♑︎ Capricorn 12:23 pm PST

──────────────── ♀♀♀   vendredo ────────────────

♑︎
♒︎   Friday
3

☽✶♂   4:22 am
♀□♅   12:37 pm
☽✶♀   1:36 pm
☽☌♉   4:56 pm   v/c
☽→♒︎   7:56 pm

──
All aspects in Pacific Standard Time; add 3 hours for EST; add 8 hours for GMT

© *Selina Di Girolamo 2000*

Awakening Four

After pawning the diamonds,
laying spades & clubs to rest,
I awaken to the fact that I am *Queen*
and live through my *heart* . . .

© *Laura A. Vousé 2000*

How to Become a We'Moon Contributor

We'Moon is an exploration of a world created in Her image. We welcome artwork by, for and about womyn. Our focus on womyn is an affirmation of the range and richness of a world where womyn are whole unto themselves. Many earth-based cultures traditionally have womyn-only spaces and times, which, through deepening the female experience, are seen to enhance womyn's contributions to the whole of society. **We'Moon** invites all womyn who love and honor womyn to join us in this spirit, and we offer what we create from such a space for the benefit of all beings.

Currently creating WE'MOON '03: GREAT MOTHER
Now accepting contributions for WE'MOON '04

If you are interested in being a **We'Moon** contributor send us a business-sized SASE (self-addressed stamped #10 envelope) or an SAE and 2 international postal coupons by August 20, 2002. We'll send you a Call for Contributions (which includes information about the theme and how to submit your art and writing) and a Release Form to return with your work. *Please do not send in any work without first receiving a Call for Contributions . . . thanks.*

How to Order WE'MOON and Mother Tongue Ink Products

Call or write to request our catalog or order direct—we take credit cards.
- **We'Moon '02** (w/ lay-flat binding: $15.95 or w/ spiral binding: $15.95)
- **We'Moon '02 Unbound** (w/ no binding for customized use: $15.95)
- **We'Moon on the Wall '02** (12" x 12", color wall calendar, 32pp: $12.95)
- **Lunar Power Packet (LPP) '02** includes 13 greeting cards w/ envelopes: $13
- **LPP '01** includes 13 greeting cards (art from **We'Moon '01**) w/ envelopes: $13
- **Shipping/handling is not included**—contact us for our new rates.

When ordering by snail mail or e-mail please include the following: a check or money order in U.S. funds made out to Mother Tongue Ink or your Master card/Visa number and expiration date *and* a note listing your name, address, phone number, and product and quantity ordered.

Mother Tongue Ink write: P.O. Box 1395-A Estacada, OR 97023 or call: 503-630-7848 or toll free 877-693-6666 (877-0 WE-MOON) or email: matrix@wemoon.ws

ACKNOWLEDGEMENTS

Putting together the **We'Moon** this year was a special challenge (see Introduction p. 28). The cumulative effect of the fire trauma and all the changes it put us through (in recreating **We'Moon '02**, our office, our business and our community home) took its toll. Despite all this, the **We'Moon** staff functioned fabulously throughout. The fact that we were able to produce this **We'Moon** at all—on time, even, is the greatest acknowledgement of our work we could have.

Beth Freewomon, now in her eleventh year working on **We'Moon**, headed up the team as We'Moonager. As usual, she was miraculously able to hold together all the threads that go into creating it and still managed to coordinate the activities of the whole staff and carry on business under the most extraordinanry circumstances. Yeah, Beth! We are blessed that Meghan Garrity joined the staff in January—just in time to be part of the whole process of creation and subsequent re-creation. Her expertise and creativity as a graphic artist, computer whiz, and journalist-editor were a great gift, as well as her willingness to work long hours and keep a fresh perspective. Amy (having just published her first novel, *Undertow*) took the helm in keeping up with e-mail correspondence and our data base, as well as being chief copy-editor and proofer. Cherie and Eagle were illustrious/industrious Co-Chiefs in the office, on the phones, filling orders, handling correspondence and all around handy womyn. Bethroot, wordwitch par excellance (now in her fifth year as 'guest editor') is an indispensible member of the Creatrix. NíAódagaín, Wyndy and Terry helped with proofing, along with all members of the staff who survived numerous production marathons. Blessings and gratitude to Gisela and Rosemarie who create the German edition of **We'Moon**. Appreciations to Hanna and Ainka, our faithful and eager Office Dogs.

A special thanks to all our artists and writers whose work was lost in the fire and who responded with so much understanding and support. Appreciations to all womyn who partook in our Weaving Circles (helping us select material for **We'Moon**)—our records burned in the fire, please contact us if you were a weaver. Also anyone who bought a **We'Moon '01** directly from us before February '01 please contact us—those records burned before we added you to our database! A special thanks and deep appreciation goes to all **We'Moon** contributors and friends who have sent (and are still sending) donations and lots of support in response to the fire. **We'Moon** is truly a community endeavor.   ¤ *Musawa 2001*

Resources Referenced throughout We'Moon

We'Mooniversity is a new non-profit tax-exempt organization created to expand upon and moonifest the ideas and visions of **We'Moon** on the land—currently raising funds to rebuild after the fire. P.O. Box 1395, Estacada, OR 97023 USA matrix@wemoon.ws   p. 31

Lori Berenson Defense: Joannie Levine is co-coordinating a speaking tour. Contact Committee to Free Lori Berenson, www.freelori.org Moon I, p. 39

Aboriginal Women Elders: Contact address—Kapupulangu Women's Law and Culture Centre, PMB 308, Wirrimanu, Halls Creek, 6770 Australia.
Moon II, p. 44

AMMA: Contact www.ammachi.org, or call the M. A. Center at 510-537-9417.   Moon III, p. 56

Revolutionary Association of the Women of Afghanistan: RAWA P.O. Box 374, Quetta, Pakistan or rawa@rawa.org www.my.rawa.org or www.rawa.org/ml.htm   Moon III, p. 59

Chiapas Solidarity: For more information visit these websites: www.mexicosolidarity.org or www.ezln.org.   Moon IV, pp. 66–67

Bloodsisters Project: Contact them at bloodsisters@chickmail.com or visit their website www.bloodsisters.org for info or www.urbanarmor.org for gear.   Moon IV, p. 75

Breast Cancer: Contact Susan G. Komen Breast Cancer 877-3079725; National Alliance of Breast Cancer Organizations www.nabco.org; National Women's Health Resource Center 877-986-9472; Hambleton Project is a cancer support center for lesbians in Portland, OR USA 503-335-6591.   Moon V, pp. 90, 91

Vandana Shiva/GMO Activism: For more information on genetically modified food (GMO's) and related issues see *Stolen Harvest*, her other books (available through www.southendpress.org) and info@nwrage.org or www.tao.ca/~ban/   Moon VII, p. 113

Mandala Dance of the 21 Taras: Visit Tara Dhatu's website at www.taradhatu.org or to sponsor a delegate emeraldtara@hotmail.com 619-223-8774. Moon VIII, p. 116

Goddess Conference, Glastonbury: Write: 2-4 High Street, Glastonbury, BA6 9DU, Somerset, England. Tel: 44(0) 1458 833933/831518 kathy.jones@ukonline.co.uk   Moon VIII, p. 124

Dyke Art Retreat Camp (DARE): founded by Siera Lonepine Briano, Jemma Crae and Jean Mountaingrove in 1990. Write Jean Mountaingrove at 2000 King Mountain Trail, Sunny Valley, OR 97497.

Moon VIII, p. 125

Forest Protection Activists: Francis Eatherington works with Umpqua Watersheds, P.O.Box 101, Roseburg, Oregon 97479; 541-672-7065 www.umpqua-watersheds.org. To find out how to get involved locally in the U.S. contact www.americanlands.org. The Native Forest Network for International contacts: www.nativeforest.org   Moon X, p. 141

Weaving a Web of Solidarity: Contact information tolle_femme@moncourrier.com. For more information on FTAA, WTO and anti-globalization events and articles, visit Starhawk's website: www.starhawk.org   Moon X, p.144

SPHere (Sustainable Peace Here): A women's empowerment project in Nepal, contact Huldah Warren: sphere@mint.net   Moon X, p. 147

Environmental Safer living: www.mindspring.com/~voiceof the earth 520-822-2643. "Environmentally Safer Living" booklet available through www.mindspring.com/~threepointspress   Moon XIII, p.175

Temple of Sekmet: Contact Patricia Pearlman, P.O. Box 946, Indian Springs, NV 89018 USA, fax: 702-879-3263, goddess@anv.net or The Foundation for a Compassionate Society c/o Genevieve Vaughn, 227 Congress Ave., Ste.100 Austin, TX, 78701 USA   Moon XIII, p. 181

COVER NOTES

Front cover art *Gaia & Daphne* **by Sandra Stanton.** Gaia was the ancient creatrix Earth Mother of the Greeks. Python coiled around the omphalos (navel) at Delphi, guarded the sacred divinatory Castalian spring and shared oracular knowledge with Gaia's priest-esses, the Pythia. When one of her priestesses, Daphne, was being pursued by Apollo, Gaia changed her into a laurel tree so she could escape from him. The laurel wreath was once considered a magical charm against evil but later became a victory symbol.

Back cover art *Sacred Thread Mandala* **by Cynthia Ré Robbins.** The Divine Source is weaving the World, spinning Her Sacred Thread, sending out Umbilical Cords of Energy, feeding the Four Directions with Her Light. All of Life is Connected, all a part of the One. The endless flow of Life, Death and Rebirth whirls as the Maiden, Mother and Crone Spiral Dance around this Pulsating Center, the Core of our Being. My oil Paintings are in the Mische Technique.

© COPYRIGHTS ¤ AND CONTACTING CONTRIBUTORS

Copyrights of individual works in **We'Moon '02** belong to each contributor. Please honor the copyrights: © means <u>do not reproduce without the express permission of the artist or author</u>. Some we'moon prefer to free the copyright on their work. ¤ means <u>this work may be passed on among women who wish to reprint it "in the spirit of We'Moon," with credit given (to them and **We'Moon**) and a copy sent to the author/artist</u>. Contributors can be contacted directly when their addresses are given in the bylines, or by sending us a letter with an envelope with sufficient postage plus $1 handling fee for each contributor to be contacted.

CONTRIBUTOR BYLINES AND INDEX*

* Each page number at the end of a byline indicates on which page you will find the contributor's work. E-mail and web site addresses are underlined; if it appears that there is a blank space it is really an underscore (_).

Candida Sea Blyth (cea) (South Devon, England) loves living by the river Dartmoor. She makes her own paint from soil, celebrating Spirit and Body! For commissions, workshops or exhibition information, contact her at earthlove_cea@yahoo.co.uk or 6 Rewlea Cotts. Ashburton, TQ137EL.   p. 4

Carol Sawyer (San Francisco, CA), having come unglued to get unstuck from the most ancient of her wounds, is moving again—with the help of divinity in the guise of many friends, she should be settling into her new home in the upper Nehalem R. Valley, OR, by September '01.   p. 111

Carol Wylie (Biggar, SK, Canada) is a visual artist living in the lovely prairies of Western Canada. Her work is about the strength and love of the unity of womyn.   p. 83

Carrie Gaylord (Portland, OR): I am currently living in Portland practicing fine arts, mothering, supporting birthing women, moon gazing, dish washing, dog walking and various other forms of meditation.   p. 151

Cheyenne Lukat (Palm City, FL) is an 8 year-old artist living on the Treasure Coast of Florida. Cheyenne lives with her mom, a midwife, her cat Max and Guinea pig Cutie. She has been doing art as long as her mom can remember.   p. 106

Chris Sitka (Melbourne, Australia) is a widely published lesbian writer, researcher, community activist and creative thinker. She set up Friends of Kapululangu Aboriginal Women's Centre to support the women elders in maintaining their traditional women's spiritual and cultural practices. csitka@jeack.com.au pp. 44,45

Christina Baldwin (Langley, WA) and her partner Ann Linnea have a vision for community they call PeerSpirit. Basing their work on Christina's book Calling the Circle, they teach PeerSpitit Circles throughout the U.S. and Canada. PO Box 550, Langley, WA 98260. www.peerspirit.com   p. 36

Christina Walczuk (Balallan, Isle of Lewis, Scotland): My work has led me to do Goddess-oriented art and I have moved to an area where my view overlooks one of the Earth Goddesses known as the "Cailleach Na Mointeach"—Gaelic for "The Old Woman of the Moors."   p. 107

Colette Gardiner (OR) is an herbalist and a plant lover. She has spent 20 years working with the green world and offers walks, classes in Eugene and Portland OR, consults, lay and professional apprenticeships. She enjoys spending time in the garden with her feline assistants.   p. 145

Colleen Redman (Floyd, VA): Member of Floyd Woman's Circle community, co-editor and regular contributor to *A Museletter*. Foster care provider for people with disabilities. Seeking properties of alphabet letter sounds. Please correspond at joklein@swva.net   p. 85

Cora Yee (Honolulu, HI)   p. 129

Corey Alicks Lie-Nielsen (Cottage Grove, OR) is a midwife, writer, earth-mother of five young children, three of whom were water-born, four at home, and is currently nursing twins! She lives in Oregon and Alaska.   p. 150

Cristina Sarasvati Carson (San Rafael, CA): Painter, photographer, healer, dancer! I am on fire! I combine art therapy, bodywork and hypnosis in my practice as a therapist. My first novel will be published next year and I am collecting wonderful friends and guides throughout this adventurous life.   pp. 87, 90

Cynthia Ré Robbins (Eureka Springs, AR): I am envisioning myself as a Painter Priestess, allowing Spirit and Mystery to pour through my being, my hand, my brush. It emerges onto the canvas, bewitching and beautiful. As it is shared with others, more goodness and light arrives in our world. www.art4spirit.com   back cover

D. Maia Huang (Oakland, CA): As an expressive artist, D. Maia Huang creates mixed media oil paintings, monoprints, photographs, poetry and crafts, resonating the visions of her inner world with a communal rhythm flowing from the generation of all cultures. She has developed a diverse body of work and is a respected professional artist of the Bay Area.   p. 128

Dánahy Sharonrose AKA Sharon Sumpter (Portland, OR) is a fairy princess masquerading as a Professional Organizer and Workshop Facilitator. Combining counseling, ceremony, Feng Shui, voluntary simplicity and her love of Mother Earth, she guides others in creating Sacred order in their lives. danahyheals@hotmail.com   p. 87

Deborah Koff-Chapin (Langley, WA): Her evocative images are created through the simple yet profound process she calls Touch Drawing. Deborah is the creator of *Soul Cards 1* and *2* and author of *Drawing Out Your Soul*. She teaches internationally and is founding director of The Center for Touch Drawing. www.soulcards.com   pp. 29, 134, 143

Deborah Le Sueur (Graton, CA): Clay, the source of life, has inspired, challenged and taught me for more than 30 years. She is where I came from and where I will return.   p. 177

Deborah Mayaan (Tucson, AZ) (formerly Debby Earthdaughter): Writing, singing, dancing, drumming, celebrating life, dreaming, drawing, being. For more about becoming the voice of the earth, please see www.mindspring.com/~voiceoftheearth   p. 175

Demetra George (Eugene, OR) is author of *Asteroid Goddesses, Astrology for Yourself, Mysteries of the Dark Moon* and *Finding Our Way through the Dark*. She incorporates archetypes, transpersonal healing and astrology in her lecturing, writing and counseling. Currently teaches the history of ancient astrology. She leads pilgrimages to ancient sites in Greece. dgeorge@orednet.org   p. 201

Diana Gardener (Eugene, OR) is a nature-loving witch, artist, activist. She feeds her spirit and honors the Goddess through ritual, drumming, dancing and gardening. She strives to appreciate diversity and feel the common spirit in all.   p. 127

Diana Tigerlily (Marion, IL): I move earth with my hands, plant magic with my family, run barefoot with my cats and rant poetry deep into the night.   p. 102

Diane Goldsmith (Nelson, BC, Canada): Our ritual group has been meeting for many years. We return to the circle again and again: a space for magic, communion; a holder of our history and our ongoing stories as women.   p. 180

Diane M.Bergstrom (Louisville, CO): I garden, create spirit masks and write from the front range of the Rocky Mountains. My essays focus on my mid-western matriarchs, such as Great Aunt Minnie, who once refused the offer of an engagement ring and requested a piano instead.   p. 63

Donna Campbell (Cumbria, England): Scottish mother, community artist and painter living in the English Lake District. Currently drawing inspiration from pregnancy, childbirth and breast feeding. I am currently totally inspired by the study of homeopathy and holistic health.   p. 156

Donna Goodwin (Santa Fe, NM) is an artist and photographer native to New Mexico. She lives in Santa Fe and you can contact her by email at mythicimage@earthlink.net   pp. 172, 174

Donna Henes (Brooklyn, NY) Urban Shaman, publishes *Always in Season: Living in Sync With the Cycles, Moon Watcher's Manual* and *Celestially Auspicious*

Occasions™. She has offered lectures, workshops, circles and celebrations world-wide for 30 years and maintains Mama Donna's Tea Garden & Healing Haven. For information, contact her at cityshaman@aol.com   p. 171

Eaglehawk (Tesuque, NM) has been living in community with wimmin for 16 years. Currently migrating with my sweetie, Musawa, between ARF land and We'Moon land. I love taking photos of wimmin, kids, animals and Big Mama Earth.   pp. 52, 130, 153

Elena Margo (Eugene, OR) makes camp in the Pacific Northwest while on an inner journey to recover harmony, joy and wonder. She finds that prayer on the path helps her to see the gifts she is constantly being given.   p. 72

Elizabeth Roberts (Nyack, NY), a witchy revolutionary, does anti-racist and anti-imperialist education and organization with Resistance in Brooklyn and The Brecht Forum. She takes leadership from her cats, Mali and Kito. Her chapbook *Brave as Planets* is available for $4. E-mail at lizard@mail.tco.com   pp. 79, 95

Elizabeth Staber (New York, NY): Currently residing in New York City, working with inner-city children. I love to take black and white photographs of women because I believe my art empowers us as a whole.   pp. 99, 100

Ellen Marie Hinchcliffe (Minneapolis, MN): First, a big shout-out to my mom who inspires me with her paintings and is the coolest! I am working on my first spoken word record. I also have zines of my poetry. I will gladly sell you stuff or just respond to various rants. ehinchcliffe@yahoo.com   p. 43

Francis Eatherington (Roseberg, OR): I monitor timber sales on Public Forests in Oregon. The Forest Service has predicted that all the old-growth forests available for logging will be clear-cut and converted to tree plantations within 50 years—on our watch.   p. 141

Frankie Hansbearry (Sacramento, CA): My inspiration is ancient art, folk art and modern art. The figurative work I create in clay, mixed media and papier-mâché reflects our strengths, weaknesses—i.e., the gamut of human character. Often, the work becomes a shrine-like center, adorned with personal objects.   pp. 41, 157

Gaia Sophia Hawkin (Kirkland, WA) lives in a glen in Kirkland where she creates altars, magical space, shrines, blessing ways and a place of healing, wholeing and holiness. Write her at gaia4444@earthlink.net   p. 158

Gail K. Nyoka (Toronto, ON, Canada): Fellowship of Isis Priestess, mother, playwright, writer, sacred circle dancer, shamanic practitioner. Conducts rites of passage, gives courses. Precept of Iseum of the Radiant Flame. kathleensnake@hotmail.com   p. 155

Genet Rose Kemp (Maple Falls, WA): I live in the Cascade Mountains and my roots extend to the Colorado Rockies. I am inspired by mountains, clay, cooking, growing food, oceans, rivers, telemark skiing and playing with my dogs—Pura Vida!   p. 140

Genevieve Vaughan (Austin, TX), born in Texas, 1939, she developed a theory of patriarchy and of a woman-led gift economy. (*For-Giving, a Feminist Criticism of Exchange*, 1997, Plain View Press). She built and maintains the Temple of Sekhmet. www.gift-economy.com   p. 181

Glennie Kindred (Brassington, Derbyshire, England) shares her joy of the Earth and her trees in her three books: *The Earth's Cycle of Celebration, The Sacred Tree* and *The Tree of Ogham*, all hand-written and illustrated in her own inimitable style. They are available from: Kindred Books, PO Box 340574, Columbus, OH 43234.   p. 123

Gretchen Lawlor (Seattle/Whidbey Island, WA) is an astrologess and naturopathic practitioner who does astrological consults in person, by mail and by phone. (360) 221-4341; light@whidbey.com; PO Box 753, Langley, WA 98260. See my quarterly predictions at www.wemoon.ws, also my work at http://glawlor.hypermart.net or starIQ.com   pp. 12, 13, Moons II–XIII

Gwen Luptak (Victoria, BC, Canada): The Goddess speaks to me through her earth energies and from her sacred sites. Her images also appear to me on the pathway of my inner journey. It is my pleasure to be able to play a part in the rebirthing of the sacred feminine image.   p. 15

Heather Rowntree (Santa Fe, NM): A choice-centered astrologer who has been counseling with astrology for 20 years.   pp. 15, 18

Helena Hinn (Whitley Bay, England): I am a writer deeply interested in women's spirituality and the ancient female mysteries and their relevance today.   p. 38

Hrana Janto (Tillson, NY) is an artist on a Goddess mission. Her Goddess paintings have appeared in 5 Llewellyn calendars. Her *The Goddess Oracle Divination* deck and book covers can be viewed at www.hranajanto.com She lives, paints and dances in NY's Hudson Valley.   p. 159

Huldah Warren (Belfast, ME) is the Executive Director and Field Advisor for SPHere (Sustainable Peace Here) encouraging compassionate responses in the west toward women and children of Nepal. She has come to recognize that to serve life is a sacred response and responsibility. sphere@mint.net   p. 147

Ildiko Cziglenyi (Trinidad, CA) is an artist and dancer. Through each of her visions she tells a story of Mother Nature's timeless mystery and wisdom, expressing the grace, power and beauty of the Goddess. For info on cards and prints: www.isledecoco.com or P.O. Box 1141, Trinidad, CA 95570   p. 93

Jan McLaughlin (Cottage Grove, OR): My passion is political art. The Burning Times (European witch-hunts) body of work includes paintings, book, slideshow/performance piece. Recent work: a combo of eco-feminism, spirituality. pp. 116, 117

Janine Canan (Sonoma, CA) is the author of *She Rises Like the Sun* and 12 other books of poetry, including *Changing Woman, Star in My Forehead: Poems by Else Lasker-Schueler,* and *The Rhyme of the Ag-ed Mariness: Last Poems of Lynn Lonidier.* All available from jancanan@vom.com or www.janinecanan.com   p. 56

Jeanne Hardy   p. 35

Jennifer Beam (Point Richmond, CA) is an artist, musician, writer and educator living in the San Francisco Bay Area with her partner, Amory, and her animal children, Max and Ming.   p. 121

Jennifer Case (San Diego, CA) is an educator, writer, consultant and arts advocate dedicated to restoring mythic memory and re-weaving the fabric of culture and community. She is an active member of Tara Dhatu, a non-profit organization. www.taradhatu.org or emeraldtara@hotmail.com   p. 114

Jessica Montgomery (San Francisco, CA) is a ceremonialist and shamanatrix relentlessly devoted to ecstatic collaboration with the Groove Ma in Her infinite guises. She also teaches internationally.   pp. 49, 101

Joan R. Riise (Chicago, IL)   p. 169

Joanie Levine (Eugene, OR) currently teaches both children and adults in an integrative arts style, combining drumming, dancing, singing, finger-painting, authentic movement and personal theater. She is also a gifted healer, political activist, gardener and writer of both poetry and prose. pp. 39, 131

Joyce Radtke (Arcata, CA): Artist, writer, ritual maker, teacher and mother—hoping to touch the world with sensitivity and respect. Feel honored to live under the arms of giant redwoods and breathe the air of the Pacific. p. 167

Julianne Skai Arbor (Santa Rosa, CA), M.A, M.S., is an environmental artist and Environmental Arts Educator. Her visionary series of medicine shields is a reflection of shamanic healing and interconnection with the Earth. She teaches an interdisciplinary program at New College of California, Santa Rosa. p. 145

Katheryn Trenshaw (Totnes, Devon, England) is an artist, workshop facilitator, mom and "midwife" of women remembering wholeness. She is an American living in the land of magical stone circles that inspire her. Originals, cards and reproductions available. P.O. Box 3 Totnes TQ95WJ UK www.ktrenshaw.com pp. 31, 112

Kathleen Gaitt (Langley, BC Canada) is a human, growing and being, who feels blessed to live in a piece of earth's garden where art, poetry and ritual circle the seasons along with the plants and creatures. p. 142

Kim Antieau (Stevenson, WA) is an ecowriter/artist who worships the earth she walks upon. p. 35

Kit Skeoch (Berkeley, CA) is a gardener and creative goddess living in Berkeley with her partner Alex and their two cats. pp. 55, 136

Lana Mareé (Nelson, BC, Canada): Small-town woman with an expansive mind and body loves to be alive. Writes because it feels good. pp. 108, 132

Laura A. Vousé (Redding, CT): Mom, yoga teacher whose mission is to help heal the planet for future generations. p. 185

Le'ema Kathleen Graham (San Rafael, CA) p. 92

Lena Bartula (Santa Fe, NM) is an artist who incorporates dreams, visions and memories to create shrine-like paintings inspired by the Great Mother. She lives in an earth house which she and her husband built out of love, sweat and recycled materials. p. 51

Lilian de Mello (Kapaa, HI): Nowadays especially interested in b&w, infrared, image & emulsion transfers, photo collages to develop "Soul Healing Imagery". Looking for emotions & the goddess aspect of women and nature. Multi-layered images searching for feelings and soul. E-mail: ldmphoto@gte.net. pp. 34, 139

Linda "Bucky" Marshall (Stillwater, OK) loves rivers so much that she now works summers as a "swamper," i.e. cook, baggage and portable toilet duties while learning to be a guide on rivers in Utah. She's also son Avery's mom. pp. 65, 135

Lisa de St. Croix (Ramah, NM) South African by birth, mother and soul mate lives at an oasis on the high desert of New Mexico. She creates paintings, visual journals, sacred spaces and rituals. She is an organizer of the El Morro Arts Council. www.lisadestcroix.com pp. 61, 119

Lorena Babcock Moore (Corona de Tucson, AZ) is an artist in hand-ground mineral pigments, a blacksmith specializing in iron jewelry and ritual bells and a geologist. www.mineralarts.com pp. 3, 173

Loretta Joseph (Victoria, BC, Canada): I started carving 11 years ago at age 51. I use 2 simple knives and "found" wood from beaches and forests and let wood, nature and my "inner eye" guide me to the finished form. Carving is my place of refuge, meditation and joy. p. 84

Luisa Teish (Oakland, CA) is a writer, performer and ritual designer. She is an initiated elder (*iyanifa, Mother of destiny*) in the Ifa/Orisha tradition and holds a chieftancy title (*yeye'woro, Great Mother of Many) from Ile-Ife, Nigeria*. Her new book is *Jump Up: Good Times Throughout the Seasons with Celebrations from Around the World* (Conari Press). www.jambalayaspirit.org   p. 109

Lynda R. Healy (Sonora, CA): Nurtured by nature in the Sierra foothills, fulfilling my childhood dream of living a creative life. Painting images of women in transition and expressing my inner visions have opened my heart and my path in life. p. 74

Lynn Creighton (Northridge, CA): I have led ceremonies for healing, including vision quests, purification lodges and prayer dances; provided retreats for teaching the sacredness of sexuality and created sculpture representing this healing with ecstatic female figures in full celebration. www.sacred-source.com   pp. 80, 81

Lynn Dewart (San Diego, CA) is an artist, guide and costumer. I honor the cycles, rhythms and stories of the inner and outer worlds and the width and breadth of the human experience. My sculptures serve as icon, avenue, totem, fetish, trophy, mirror. www.lynndewart.com   p. 46

Mara Friedman (Lorane, OR): Roots deepen as I continue my expression of awe and gratitude through paintings honoring the Sacred Feminine aspect of Spirit. For a catalog of cards and prints, contact me at www.newmoonvisions.com pp. 71, 89, 108

Marcia Starck (Santa Fe, NM) is a Medical Astrologer, Healer and Medicine teacher who does astrological counseling, teaches classes and conducts rituals. Her books, *Handbook of Natural Therapies, Astrology—Key to Holistic Health, Healing with Astrology* and others are available at: POB 5435, Santa Fe, NM 87502. (505) 983-8779 earthmed@aol.com www.earthmedicineways.com   p. 71

Marguerite Bartley (Ballydehob, Co. Cork, Ireland): Writing brings me satisfaction and contentment, release and connection. I enjoy designing and selling my handcrafted cards. Friends and family are deep in my heart but my deepest contentment is in my living alone. I travel a little. Value my computer. Life is good and the years are precious.   p. 52

Mari Susan Selby (Santa Fe, NM) is a poet of the Earth, a Dakini of strong laughter and an astrologer of individual and planetary evolution. Soon to be published, *Dance of the Dakinis: Freedom Oracle* with images by Jennet Inglis. 505-992-8072. PO Box 8736, Santa Fe, NM, 87504.   p. 200

Marie Perret (Sergeac, France): English artist and teacher living in France—loving nature, colours, and life! Would love contact info for women artists on the West Coast of the U.S. as I'm planning to visit. vallonperret@wanadoo.fr   p. 160

Marj Greenhut (Baston, OR) is a multi-media liver and a true Libra—trying to balance cronedom through being an artist/photographer, therapist, and landowner, creating safe women's space with her lover.   p. 125

Marna (Portland, OR) breathes in ease, inspiration, repose; exhales creativity and galactic love. Plays with star people and frolics with earth people. Come visit the Womyn's Temple in Portland and come Full Circle!   p. 77

Mary Feagan (Duluth, GA), once a nun, now an artist and writer, is owning her beauty, joy and outrageousness as she learns in her bones she is her own Promised Land. p. 99

Max Dashu (Oakland, CA) is an artist and founder of the Suppressed Histories Archives, a global women's studies project (now in its 31st year) at www.suppressedhistories.net See her paintings of bold and spirited women at www.maxdashu.net   p. 25

Maya Dobroth (Austin, TX) p. 37

Maya White Sparks (Winchester, VA): The Priestess archetype has energized my work as a devotee of The Great Mother. I assist others through natural health consultations, meditation, hypnosis, energy work, tarot. The recording, "Meditation With Maya," is available at P.O. Box 248, Flint Hill, VA 22627. p. 183

Melissa McConnell (Bellingham, WA) gives so much thanks for the abundance and blessings in her life: art, music, clay, dance, healing, words, guitar, drums, burke, family, friendship, the earth, madrona trees, laughter, breath and constant inspiration and support. moonsoleil@aol.com pp. 2, 86

Monica Sjöö (Bristol, UK): Swedish-born artist and writer and ecofeminist activist. Co-author with Barbara Mor of *The Great Cosmic Mother* and sole author of *Return of the Dark/Light Mother or New Age Armageddon* and *The Norse Goddess*. She is involved in Goddess Earth Mysteries in Britain and is rediscovering ancient Sweden. pp. 20, 32, 48, 181

Musawa (Nozama Mu): Travelling between the worlds of We'Moon Land in Oregon, rebuilding after the fire, and New Mexico Women's Land, getting back to my writing, hoping to slow down soon: paradigm shift! pp. 8, 11, 21, 23, 27, 28, 52

Nadine C. Butterfield (Mt. Vernon, NY): Seeking, praying, turning inside out . . . seeing what emerges, asking no questions—to see what flows from grace, reflecting the souls of all womyn—their mysteries, beauty, wisdom, passion, diversity, earth mothers, peace keepers . . . may we be guided on our way. pp. 6, 18, 163, 178

Nancy Bennett (B.C, Canada): Child of the Goddess, Founder of Hago and co-editor of *Hicks (Hags in the Country and Kin)*. Can be reached at bennett@sinc.com p. 70

Nell Wagenaar (Portland, OR) is a writer, artist, musician and mom, settling into urban life working for Portland's Neighborhood Mediation Center. p. 27

Niamh Leonard (Killala, Ireland) p. 97

Nicola Holmes (Peterborough, ON, Canada) is a dancing spirit, living her ever-changing questions as joyfully as possible. She values balance, the still point and silence. p. 125

Nitanju Bolade Casel (Silver Spring, MD) p. 137

Patricia Pearlman (Indian Springs, NV) has been the caregiver and priestess of the Sekhmet Temple since 1994. She's a crone and proud of it. She can perform legal handfasting (weddings) at the Temple and also conducts Pagan celebrations. goddess@anv.net p. 181

Patricia Worth (Las Vegas, NV) is a founding member of and staff writer for Nurses for the Rights of the Child, a non-profit human rights organization dedicated to promoting genital integrity for all children. nurses.cirp.org bonedancer@plateautel.net p. 118

Paula Billups (Webster, TX): A Texas chica watching my power grow and enthusiastically welcoming each new silver thread on my head. Bless you! p. 168

Paula Bristol (Roseville, CA): Catholic Mother/Artist/Poet imagiCing a world where our sons can be nurturing and our daughters can be strong! I'm trying to LIVE and LOVE in the "suburbs." Merry Be and Mary Bless! p. 104

Peggy Sue McRae (Friday Harbor, WA) p. 182

Phoenix B. Grace (Columbus, OH), thirty-four, spirals with the Goddess . . . I find myself blessed with the sweet, constant companionship of my cat-daughter-friend, Sheba, the warm solidarity of my blood sisters, the absolute glory of my priestess training and the magnificent wholeness of my soul! p. 53

Puma Lichtblau (Hildesheim, Denmark): Born as ♈, asc ♒ 1952, newborn as lesbian '74, traveling a lot, living on wemon's land in Denmark, caring for old wemon, cooking for groups, learning Breathing Therapie and finally in '96 I allowed the artist to come out. Thank you!   p. 161

Radhia A. Jaaber (Woodbridge, VA) uses her own life experiences as a guide in developing her rhythmic art, writing. Using writing as a natural way to create healing, transformation and liberation—interweaving a medley of images of spirituality, dialogue, women's liberation struggle and indigenous lore.   p. 55

Rose Flint (Larkhall, Bath, England): Poet, artist, teacher, art therapist. I am a Priestess of Avalon and celebrate at the Goddess Conference in Glastonbury with many other wild women—priestesses, sisters, mothers, daughters, crones.   p. 124

Ruby Juices (Oakland, CA) is an artist, workshop facilitator and community ritual leader. She offers workshops in Sacred Sexuality and Sexual Empowerment for women. rogue_ruby@yahoo.com   p. 80

Ruth Barrett (Monona, WI) is a Dianic high priestess, ritualist, educator and award-winning recording artist of original Goddess songs. She teaches ritual arts internationally and invites you to visit her website for more info: www.womensriteswomensmysteries.com   p. 155

Sandra Pastorius (Santa Cruz, CA): I published the *Lunar Muse—a Monthly Moon Guide* for ten years. I continue to offer spiritual guidance as an astrologer, ceremonialist and mentor. PO Box 2344, Santa Cruz, CA 95063.   p. 200

Sandra Stanton (Farmington, ME) is inspired by a great love of mother earth, has been painting the Goddess and Her creatures for many years. Her work can be seen at www.goddessmyths.com. Prints are available from her at 180 Main St., Suite 336 Farmington, ME 04938.   front cover

Sara Joy Fishkin (Oakland, CA) sees the connections between our human bodies and the Earth body through whom we live. She strives to express these relationships through farming, herbalism, art and poetry. Her mind works best when her hands are active.   p. 66

Sara-Lou Klein (Denver, CO) is an artist who is inspired by and grateful for rocks and sticks and flowers and shells and rusty and her family and her friends and her cats and her circle with no name. Blessed BEe.   p. 164

Sarah Teofanov (Farmington, NM) is a cultural risk taker/mythmaker whose work concentrates on women's myth and the need to reinvent a new sustainable earth-friendly one. She lives in New Mexico with her family.   p. 109

Schar Cbear Freeman (Kaua'i, HI) is an American Native/Spanish visual artist; painting, photography, performance poetry and Art of Soul instructor. "Artists are the record-keepers for our coming generations and should have something to offer each and every day from the wholeness of our hearts." www.scharcbear.8k.com email: et schar@gateway.net   pp. 103, 166

Selina Di Girolamo (Chiltern Hills, England) is a womb-in artist, priestess to the Dark Mother, poet, mother of sons, witch. Reclaiming endarkenment and celebrating wombscape. Contact her at selinawitch@darkmother.co.uk www.darkmother.co.uk or www.di-girolamo.co.uk   pp. 149, 185

Sequoia Megary Sigler (Baltimore, MD) is a tree-hugging, proud dyke-feminist, artist, poet, teacher and strong survivor who works and prays for the safety of children and all living things!   p. 62

Sharon Hart (Burlington, VT) p. 73

Shekhinah Mountainwater (Santa Cruz, CA) is a radical lesbian feminist witch, muse and faery bard, composer and singer of songs, myths, prayers and poetry—author of *Ariadne's Thread*. Creatrix of her own Goddess tarot deck, she is available for readings in person, online or by telephone. shekhinahmoon@aol.com or (831) 423-7639 or P.O. Box 2991, Santa Cruz, CA 95063. p. 159

Shirley Kishiyama (Portland, OR) is a Portland poet whose work has appeared in diverse publications like Journal of Medical Humanities, American Tanka, Frontiers and three anthologies. p. 172

Shoshana Rothaizer (Flushing, NY) is a Native New Yorker who has sojourned and traveled in various parts of North America and Europe. She enjoys connecting with the spirits of nature in both city and country. Many of Shoshana's best-known images were taken on lesbian land. For info on photo postcards, please send a SASE to 147-44 69th Road, Flushing, NY 11367-1732. pp. 78, 122, 123

Starhawk (San Francisco, CA) peace activist and one of the foremost voices of eco-feminism. Her lectures and workshops draw on her 25 years of research and experience in the Goddess movement. She is author of many books, has consulted on several films and is currently co-writing a workbook for Reclaiming Traditional Magic. p. 144

Stephanie Griffis (Boulder Creek, CA): I have composed poetry since 2nd grade. A young mother of two, I left the east and came to Oregon. Performer/teacher for 22 years in the U.S. and Central America. A Radar Angel, free-spirit, goddess inspired. Now living in California. p. 51

Sue Silvermarie (Onalaska, WI): Write me at ssilvermarie@yahoo.com pp. 88, 105

Susan Levitt (San Francisco, CA) is a witch and author of *Taoist Feng Shui* and *Taoist Astrology*. She works as a Tarot card reader, astrologer and feng shui consultant in S.F. Visit her web site at www.susanlevitt.com or call 415-642-8019. pp. 22, 23, 24

Susan Raven Perri (Rochester, NY) is an herbalist, author, and mother cultivating the good life in Hawai'i. Please be in touch for more info on home study, tinctures, flower essences, and books at www.bcbotanica.com p. 25

Tina Smale (Hereford UK): I am mainly a political and visual culture jammer who likes to take time out to revisit my pagan and spiritual roots artistically. I live in beautiful countryside which inspires me to do this. My e-mail is tween40@hotmail.com. p. 53

Tracy Litterick (S.Yorks, England): I am inspired by wild women, witches, the magic of homeopathy and the beautiful moors surrounding my city. I'm exploring the inner world on my healing journey through my images of animal spirit, dreams, and ancient women's cultures. p. 8

Ursula Stricker (Oberdiessbach, Switzerland) dancing visual artist and teacher for placement dance, creative process. Collaboration with nature—figurines as mes-senger . . . Directs the Etage: A Space for Movement Expression and Silence in Bern, Switzerland. Works and travels in Switzerland, Italy and USA. p. 94

Vandana Shiva (New Delhi, India) is a world-renowned environmental thinker and activist. A leader in the International Forum on Globalization, Shiva won the Alternative Nobel Peace Prize (the Right Livelihood Award) in 1993. Director of the Research Foundation for Science, Technology, and Natural Resource Policy, she is the author of many books. p. 113

ECLIPSES

Eclipses demonstrate deep processes of transformation. They crack open doors to our true selves. Eclipses remind us that we are indeed not in control of our lives and that our choices manifest in our response to external stimuli. We can either recognize our fantastic natures and grow like wild flowers, or react to our external world with fear of change. We can use the alignment of the sun, moon and earth as a great ally in our own process of deep transformation. Since ancient times, astrologers have used the eclipse as a means of prediction. To determine the effect of a specific eclipse, check your natal chart and find out in what house the eclipse falls. Each house governs a specific activity or area. The effects of an eclipse are felt whether it's visible or not.

A solar eclipse is a conjunction of the Sun and Moon (new moon) and can be either total, partial or annular. A lunar eclipse is an opposition of the Sun and Moon (full moon) and can be either total, partial or appulse. The dates for the 2002 eclipses are May 26, June 10, June 24, Nov. 19 and Dec. 3. See particular dates for eclipse types and places from which they are visible. © *Mari Susan Selby 2000*

RETURN TO SOURCE: MERCURY RETROGRADE ☿℞

The cycle of the wing-footed messenger, Mercury, represents our mental and communicative life processes. This companion dancer to the sun (never traveling more than 28° away) inspires mobility and adaptability. Mercury retrogrades three or four times a year, each time in a sign of the same element. During this passage, lasting 20 to 28 days, our attention moves to unfinished business. Since all backward movement symbolizes a return to source, we can use these times to attend to our inner perceptions and reconnect with the spiritual source of our thoughts.

In 2002 Mercury retrogrades three times while in each of the Air signs, highlighting communication and mind. Since the sun will be in earth signs when the reversals begin, use practical channels for any delays or diversions. During the period from Jan. 18 to Feb. 8 we are challenged to re-align our connections, to both inner and outer Aquarian technologies. When Mercury reverses our Gemini synapses from May 15 to June 8, we exchange curious other points of view in novel ways—get creative and appease the trickster! Then from Sept. 14 to Oct. 6, when Mercury asks us to convey the unsaid and unsung, use Libran loving kindness and share wisdoms—remember friendships rule! © *Sandra Pastorius 2000*

ASTEROIDS

The asteroids, a belt of planetary bodies orbiting in the solar system mostly between Mars and Jupiter, were discovered in the early 1800's. Since the sighting of new planets in the solar system corresponds to the activation of new centers of consciousness in the human psyche, the discovery of these planetary bodies, carrying the names of hundreds of goddesses, points to an awakening of a feminine-defined principle.

Because traditional astrology uses a ten-planet system (and only two of these symbols, the Moon and Venus, represent feminine archetypes), it has, by default not had a set of symbols by which to describe other avenues of feminine expression. It has tried to fit all other women's experiences into masculine-defined archetypes.

The asteroids signify new archetypal symbols in the astrological language and they specifically address the current psychological and social issues that are arising in today's world due to the activation of the feminine principle. Synchronistic with the publication of the asteroid goddess ephemeris, the forefront of the women's movement emerged into society. At this time new aspects of feminine expression began to enter into human consciousness. Women became imbued with the possibilities of feminine creativity and intelligence that expanded and transcended the traditional roles of wife and mother (Venus and the Moon). This also marked a time of the rediscovery of women's ancient history, the growth of women's culture and sexuality independent of men, and the rebirth of the Goddess in women's spirituality.

The mandala of asteriod goddesses, on the following page, can help us to better understand the meanings of Ceres, Pallas, Juno and Vesta (the first four asteroids discovered). The large circle in the mandala represents the Moon, which is the foundation of the feminine principle and contains potential expressions of the feminine nature. Behind the Moon resides the Sun. The union of these two energies gives rise to what mystics define as "oneness." In the center of the mandala resides Venus, the core essence of the feminine nature in her activated form, who embodies the well-spring of feminine creative, magnetic, sexual, reproductive vital life force. Venus is surrounded by Ceres, Pallas, Vesta and Juno who represent the primary relationships of a woman's life—that of mother, daughter, sister and partner, respectively. Each asteroid utilizes the creative sexual energy of Venus at the center of the circle in her own unique way, as she expresses various functions and activities of the feminine principle. They are placed at the four cardinal directions of the mandala. In the horoscope this fourfold division is designated by the four angles: the Ascendent and Descendent, which define the line of the horizon, and the Midheaven and Nadir, which mark the meridian line.

Ceres, as the Great Mother and Goddess of agriculture, gives birth to the world of physical form; she births children and provides food for their survival. As the Nadir (IC) she represents a point of foundation, roots, and family.

Pallas Athene, as the daughter and the Goddess of Wisdom, generates mental and artistic creations from her mind. At the Midheaven (MC), where visible and socially useful accomplishments are realized, she represents the principle of creative intelligence.

Vesta, as the Sister, is the Temple Priestess and is a virgin in the original sense of being whole and complete in oneself. As the Ascendant (ASC.), Vesta corresponds to the Self. She signifies the principle of spiritual focus and devotion to following one's calling.

Juno, as the Goddess of Partnership, fosters and sustains union with a partner. Placed at the Descendant (DESC.), the point of one-to-one relationships, Juno symbolizes the principle of relatedness and commitment to the other. © *Demetra George 1996 excerpted and reprinted from* Asteroid Goddesses Natal Report *(a software program published by Astrolabe)*

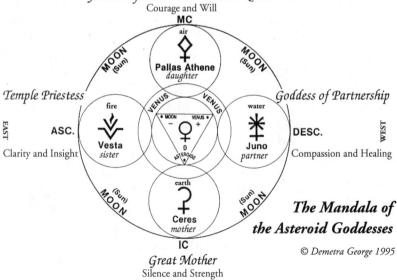

SOUTH

Goddess of Wisdom & Warrior Queen
Courage and Will

Temple Priestess
Clarity and Insight

Goddess of Partnership
Compassion and Healing

EAST

WEST

The Mandala of the Asteroid Goddesses

© *Demetra George 1995*

IC

Great Mother
Silence and Strength

NORTH

2002 ASTEROID EPHEMERIS

2002	Ceres 1	Pallas 2	Juno 3	Vesta 4
JAN 1	09≈37.8	15↑23.7	29♈54.0	28♈30.4
11	13 25.8	19 14.0	28♏57.8	27♉50.8
21	17 17.4	23 01.9	27 14.7	27♉55.6
31	21 11.4	26 46.4	24 57.1	28 42.0
FEB 10	25 06.8	00≈26.4	22 22.4	00♊05.3
20	29 02.6	04 00.7	19 51.4	02 00.6
MAR 2	02✶57.8	07 28.0	17 43.5	04 23.0
12	06 51.6	10 47.1	16 12.1	07 07.9
22	10 43.1	13 56.4	15 23.6	10 11.8
APR 1	14 31.1	16 54.2	15D18.6	13 31.4
11	18 15.0	19 38.9	15 53.7	17 04.0
21	21 53.5	22 08.0	17 04.6	20 47.5
MAY 1	25 25.4	24 19.2	18 45.8	24 40.1
11	28 49.6	26 09.8	20 52.0	28 40.1
21	02♈04.5	27 36.6	23 19.0	02♋46.5
31	05 08.5	28 36.2	26 03.0	06 58.2
JUN 10	07 59.6	29 05.4	29 00.8	11 14.2
20	10 35.5	29R01.0	02♐09.9	15 34.0
30	12 53.6	28 21.1	05 28.0	19 56.7
JUL 10	14 50.9	27 05.3	08 53.3	24 21.9
20	16 23.7	25 16.5	12 24.6	28 49.1
30	17 28.7	23 01.3	16 00.3	03♌17.7
AUG 9	18 02.2	20 29.9	19 39.5	07 47.3
19	18R00.8	17 55.2	23 21.4	12 17.5
29	17 23.3	15 31.1	27 04.9	16 47.5
SEP 8	16 10.2	13 28.9	00≈49.4	21 17.1
18	14 26.0	11 57.2	04 34.0	25 45.5
28	12 19.9	11 00.0	08 18.1	00♍11.8
OCT 8	10 04.3	10 38.3	12 00.9	04 35.4
18	07 54.2	10D50.7	15 41.5	08 55.2
28	06 03.4	11 34.3	19 21.1	13 09.9
NOV 7	04 42.2	12 45.6	22 52.7	17 18.3
17	03 57.3	14 21.3	26 21.2	21 18.3
27	03D50.7	16 17.8	29 43.4	25 08.2
DEC 7	04 21.3	18 32.1	02♑57.8	28 45.3
17	05 26.5	21 01.4	06 02.9	02♎06.5
27	07 08.0	23 43.2	08 56.8	05 08.2
JAN 6	09♈05.1	26≈35.6	11♑37.4	07♎46.1

2002	Sappho 80	Amor 1221	Pandora 55	Icarus 1566
JAN 1	18♍04.7	03≈52.2	01R09.3	29♌33.9
11	16♍10.6	09 29.5	28♋57.4	06♍40.7
21	13 42.9	14 56.0	26 36.4	12 55.6
31	10 58.3	20 12.1	24 23.3	18 32.2
FEB 10	08 16.7	25 18.7	22 32.4	23 39.4
20	05 57.2	00✶16.0	21 14.4	28 22.2
MAR 2	04 13.9	05 04.2	20 34.4	02≈43.9
12	03 13.5	09 43.6	20D32.9	06 46.4
22	02D57.5	14 14.1	21 08.1	10 30.3
APR 1	03 23.3	18 35.3	22 16.0	13 55.2
11	04 26.0	22 47.3	23 52.2	17 00.1
21	06 00.9	26 49.4	25 49.4	19 42.4
MAY 1	08 02.7	00♈41.0	28 13.5	21 58.8
11	10 26.4	04 21.3	00♌51.2	23 44.3
21	13 09.9	07 49.2	03 42.9	24 51.4
31	16 08.2	11 03.2	06 46.0	25R10.6
JUN 10	19 12.9	14 01.9	08 55.6	24 29.3
20	22 40.9	16 43.0	13 16.6	22 31.9
30	26 11.2	19 03.8	16 45.4	18 59.7
JUL 10	29 48.7	21 01.4	20 16.9	13 43.7
20	03♎32.3	22 31.8	23 52.3	06 49.6
30	07 20.7	23 31.0	27 30.6	28♋55.8
AUG 9	11 13.1	23 54.4	01♌10.0	21 05.6
19	15 08.6	23R37.6	04 52.6	14 22.5
29	19 06.9	22 37.8	08 34.5	09 21.3
SEP 8	23 06.9	20 54.4	12 16.3	06 06.8
18	27 06.0	18 31.4	15 56.8	04 27.0
28	01♎05.5	15 38.8	19 35.3	04D05.5
OCT 8	05 11.0	12 31.8	23 11.0	04 46.6
18	09 11.5	09 29.2	26 42.6	06 18.5
28	13 10.2	06 48.6	00♍09.1	08 31.7
NOV 7	17 06.5	04 43.3	03 29.2	11 19.7
17	20 59.1	03 21.0	06 41.3	14 38.2
27	24 47.0	02 43.5	09 43.6	18 22.9
DEC 7	28 28.9	02D48.3	12 34.3	22 29.7
17	02≈03.2	03 33.3	15 10.7	26 46.2
27	05 28.2	04 51.9	17 30.4	00≈22.4
JAN 6	08♏41.8	06♈40.1	19♍30.3	28♋R05.1

2002	Psyche 16	Eros 433	Lilith 1181	Toro 1685
JAN 1	18♍35.2	22♈54.9	11♐13.3	06♊42.5
11	18R44.1	29 21.4	13 57.4	10 59.6
21	18 18.2	05♉39.3	16 25.2	14 52.2
31	17 18.2	11 48.8	18 33.6	18 17.0
FEB 10	15 47.7	17 50.1	20 19.9	21 09.8
20	13 53.9	23 43.4	21 40.4	24 24.3
MAR 2	11 47.6	29 28.5	22 31.9	24 53.2
12	09 41.4	05♊05.7	22 51.5	25 28.0
22	07 47.5	10 34.8	22R36.8	24R58.8
APR 1	06 16.4	15 55.3	21 47.4	23 18.2
11	05 14.2	21 07.2	20 25.5	20 23.6
21	04 44.4	26 09.6	18 36.4	16 23.8
MAY 1	04D47.1	01♋01.8	16 29.5	11 43.8
11	05 20.3	05 43.0	14 16.3	06 59.5
21	06 21.6	10 11.3	12 09.5	02 48.9
31	07 47.4	14 24.9	10 20.6	29♈38.8
JUN 10	09 34.5	18 21.3	08 58.0	27 39.8
20	11 40.2	21 56.4	08 06.4	26 51.6
30	14 01.5	25 06.1	07D46.9	27D06.6
JUL 10	16 36.0	27 43.8	08 03.1	28 15.6
20	19 21.9	29 41.2	08 47.7	00♊10.1
30	22 17.2	00♌48.7	09 56.6	02 42.4
AUG 9	25 20.4	00R54.3	11 35.6	05 46.8
19	28 30.2	29♋46.5	13 32.8	09 18.9
29	01♎45.2	27 19.9	15 48.2	13 15.3
SEP 8	05 04.6	23 40.1	18 19.5	17 33.8
18	08 27.2	19 14.5	21 04.1	22 13.0
28	11 52.0	14 48.4	24 00.3	27 11.8
OCT 8	15 18.1	11 08.8	27 06.5	02♋30.3
18	18 44.6	08 50.1	00♑21.1	08 08.9
28	22 10.4	08D09.9	03 42.6	14 08.2
NOV 7	25 35.7	08 46.8	07 10.0	20 29.9
17	28 59.1	10 49.3	10 42.0	27 16.0
27	02♏12.9	13 58.9	14 17.6	04♍28.7
DEC 7	05 24.6	18 05.0	17 55.8	12 11.4
17	08 29.2	22 59.5	21 36.4	20 27.7
27	11 25.1	28 34.8	25 15.6	29 21.4
JAN 6	14♏10.4	04♉45.8	29♐55.3	08≈57.2

2002	Diana 78	Hidalgo 944	Urania 30	Chiron 2060
JAN 1	07♈34.6	18♑47.6	05≈41.1	02♑09.8
11	10 09.4	20 44.6	07 22.5	03 13.4
21	13 08.9	22 42.7	08 28.0	04 14.7
31	16 29.3	24 40.2	08 53.3	05 12.7
FEB 10	20 07.7	26 35.7	08R35.2	06 06.3
20	24 01.6	28 27.6	07 32.6	06 54.5
MAR 2	28 08.6	00♈14.4	05 49.6	07 36.4
12	02♉27.3	01 54.4	03 35.1	08 11.3
22	06 55.8	03 25.9	01 03.7	08 38.3
APR 1	11 32.9	04 47.0	28♑33.6	08 57.0
11	16 17.4	05 56.1	26 21.8	09 07.1
21	21 08.5	06 50.9	24 41.5	09R08.1
MAY 1	26 03.2	07 29.7	23 40.7	09 00.6
11	01♊07.0	07 50.5	23D21.3	08 44.8
21	06 13.1	07R51.7	23 42.4	08 21.7
31	11 23.1	07 32.2	24 39.8	07 52.3
JUN 10	16 34.4	06 51.4	26 09.5	07 18.0
20	21 45.5	05 49.8	28 07.1	06 40.5
30	27 10.8	04 29.6	00≈28.3	06 01.5
JUL 10	02♋31.0	02 54.2	03 09.4	05 23.2
20	07 52.5	01 08.7	06 07.6	04 47.1
30	13 14.6	29♐19.4	09 20.0	04 15.3
AUG 9	18 37.0	27 32.9	12 44.5	03 48.7
19	23 58.8	25 56.0	16 19.5	03 29.1
29	29 19.2	24 34.3	20 03.1	03 17.1
SEP 8	04♌37.7	23 31.7	23 54.3	03D13.2
18	09 52.9	22 51.1	27 51.9	03 17.9
28	15 03.7	22 33.3	01♈54.7	03 31.0
OCT 8	20 09.1	22D38.3	06 02.2	03 52.2
18	25 07.1	23 05.1	10 13.4	04 21.2
28	29 56.0	23 52.1	14 27.9	04 57.3
NOV 7	04♍33.7	24 57.6	18 43.8	05 39.7
17	08 57.2	26 19.4	23 01.6	06 27.6
27	13 03.7	27 55.6	27 21.0	07 20.1
DEC 7	16 49.2	29 44.2	01♉38.8	08 16.1
17	20 09.2	01♑43.3	05 56.5	09 14.7
27	22 58.6	03 51.1	10 13.8	10 14.7
JAN 6	25♍11.6	06≈06.0	14♉26.2	11♑15.3

Giving the positions of asteroids every
ten days in LONGITUDE at 00:00 GMT

Noon Planetary Ephemeris: GMT* January 2002

Day	Sid.Time	☉	0 hr ☽	Noon ☽	True ☊	☿	♀	♂	♃	♄	♅	♆	♇
1 Tu	18 43 51	10♑53 33	1♌ 6 24	8♌22 21	27♊ 9.1	26♑21.3	7♑47.4	17♓14.8	10♋35.9	9♊17.5	22♒28.9	7♒27.7	16♐ 3.2
2 W	18 47 48	11 54 41	15 39 38	22 57 26	27R 7.2	27 53.2	9 2.9	17 58.7	10R27.8	9R13.8	22 31.7	7 29.8	16 5.4
3 Th	18 51 45	12 55 49	0♍15 1	7♍31 38	27 5.2	29 23.9	10 18.4	18 42.6	10 19.7	9 10.1	22 34.5	7 31.9	16 7.5
4 F	18 55 41	13 56 58	14 46 39	21 59 29	27 3.6	0♒53.2	11 33.9	19 26.5	10 11.6	9 6.5	22 37.4	7 34.0	16 9.6
5 Sa	18 59 38	14 58 6	29 9 40	6♎16 49	27 2.6	2 20.7	12 49.4	20 10.4	10 3.5	9 3.0	22 40.3	7 36.2	16 11.7
6 Su	19 3 34	15 59 15	13♎20 39	20 21 0	27D 2.4	3 46.1	14 4.9	20 54.3	9 55.5	8 59.6	22 43.2	7 38.3	16 13.7
7 M	19 7 31	17 0 25	27 17 43	4♏10 46	27 3.1	5 8.9	15 20.3	21 38.1	9 47.4	8 56.2	22 46.2	7 40.5	16 15.8
8 Tu	19 11 27	18 1 34	11♏ 0 11	17 45 59	27 4.5	6 28.7	16 35.8	22 22.0	9 39.5	8 53.0	22 49.2	7 42.6	16 17.9
9 W	19 15 24	19 2 44	24 28 14	1♐ 7 4	27 6.0	7 45.0	17 51.3	23 5.9	9 31.5	8 49.8	22 52.2	7 44.8	16 19.9
10 Th	19 19 20	20 3 53	7♐42 33	14 14 46	27 7.4	8 57.0	19 6.8	23 49.7	9 23.6	8 46.7	22 55.2	7 47.0	16 21.9
11 F	19 23 17	21 5 3	20 43 51	27 9 51	27R 7.9	10 4.1	20 22.3	24 33.6	9 15.8	8 43.7	22 58.3	7 49.2	16 23.9
12 Sa	19 27 14	22 6 12	3♑32 52	9♑52 58	27 7.2	11 5.6	21 37.8	25 17.4	9 8.0	8 40.8	23 1.4	7 51.4	16 25.9
13 Su	19 31 10	23 7 21	16 10 14	22 24 43	27 5.2	12 0.6	22 53.3	26 1.2	9 0.3	8 38.0	23 4.5	7 53.6	16 27.8
14 M	19 35 7	24 8 30	28 36 31	4♒45 44	27 1.7	12 48.3	24 8.8	26 45.0	8 52.7	8 35.3	23 7.6	7 55.8	16 29.8
15 Tu	19 39 3	25 9 38	10♒52 29	16 56 54	26 57.1	13 27.8	25 24.2	27 28.8	8 45.2	8 32.7	23 10.7	7 58.1	16 31.7
16 W	19 43 0	26 10 45	22 59 12	28 59 34	26 51.7	13 58.1	26 39.7	28 12.6	8 37.7	8 30.2	23 13.9	8 0.3	16 33.6
17 Th	19 46 56	27 11 52	4♓58 16	10♓55 35	26 46.1	14 18.6	27 55.1	28 56.4	8 30.4	8 27.8	23 17.1	8 2.6	16 35.5
18 F	19 50 53	28 12 58	16 51 54	22 47 34	26 41.0	14R28.3	29 10.6	29 40.1	8 23.1	8 25.5	23 20.3	8 4.8	16 37.3
19 Sa	19 54 49	29 14 4	28 43 1	4♈38 45	26 36.9	14 26.8	0♒26.0	0♈23.9	8 16.0	8 23.3	23 23.6	8 7.1	16 39.1
20 Su	19 58 46	0♒15 8	10♈35 15	16 33 4	26 34.2	14 13.7	1 41.5	1 7.6	8 8.9	8 21.2	23 26.8	8 9.3	16 41.0
21 M	20 2 43	1 16 12	22 32 48	28 35 0	26D 33.1	13 48.9	2 56.9	1 51.3	8 2.0	8 19.2	23 30.1	8 11.6	16 42.7
22 Tu	20 6 39	2 17 14	4♉40 19	10♉49 20	26 33.4	13 12.8	4 12.3	2 34.9	7 55.2	8 17.3	23 33.3	8 13.8	16 44.5
23 W	20 10 36	3 18 16	17 2 40	23 20 54	26 34.8	12 26.1	5 27.7	3 18.6	7 48.5	8 15.5	23 36.6	8 16.1	16 46.3
24 Th	20 14 32	4 19 17	29 44 36	6♊14 13	26 36.4	11 29.9	6 43.1	4 2.2	7 41.9	8 13.8	23 40.0	8 18.4	16 48.0
25 F	20 18 29	5 20 17	12♊50 11	19 32 48	26 37.6	10 25.8	7 58.4	4 45.8	7 35.5	8 12.3	23 43.3	8 20.7	16 49.7
26 Sa	20 22 25	6 21 15	26 22 17	3♋18 39	26R 37.6	9 15.6	9 13.8	5 29.4	7 29.2	8 10.8	23 46.6	8 22.9	16 51.4
27 Su	20 26 22	7 22 13	10♋21 48	17 31 25	26 35.9	8 1.6	10 29.2	6 13.0	7 23.1	8 9.4	23 50.0	8 25.2	16 53.0
28 M	20 30 18	8 23 10	24 47 1	2♌ 7 54	26 32.1	6 46.0	11 44.5	6 56.5	7 17.1	8 8.2	23 53.4	8 27.5	16 54.6
29 Tu	20 34 15	9 24 6	9♌33 14	17 1 57	26 26.5	5 30.9	12 59.9	7 40.0	7 11.2	8 7.1	23 56.8	8 29.8	16 56.2
30 W	20 38 12	10 25 0	24 32 57	2♍ 5 0	26 19.7	4 18.6	14 15.2	8 23.5	7 5.5	8 6.1	24 0.1	8 32.1	16 57.8
31 Th	20 42 8	11 25 54	9♍36 52	17 7 21	26 12.6	3 10.7	15 30.5	9 6.9	6 59.9	8 5.1	24 3.6	8 34.3	16 59.4

Longitude February 2002

Day	Sid.Time	☉	0 hr ☽	Noon ☽	True ☊	☿	♀	♂	♃	♄	♅	♆	♇
1 F	20 46 5	12♒26 47	24♍35 20	1♎59 50	26♊ 6.2	2♒ 8.8	16♒45.8	9♈50.3	6♋54.5	8♊ 4.3	24♒ 7.0	8♒36.6	17♐ 0.9
2 Sa	20 50 1	13 27 39	9♎20 1	16 35 14	26R 1.3	1R14.0	18 1.1	10 33.7	6R49.3	8R 3.7	24 10.4	8 38.9	17 2.4
3 Su	20 53 58	14 28 31	23 45 1	0♏49 7	25 58.4	0 27.2	19 16.4	11 17.1	6 44.2	8 3.1	24 13.8	8 41.2	17 3.8
4 M	20 57 54	15 29 21	7♏47 22	14 39 51	25D 57.4	29♑48.6	20 31.6	12 0.4	6 39.3	8 2.6	24 17.2	8 43.4	17 5.3
5 Tu	21 1 51	16 30 11	21 26 41	28 8 7	25 57.9	29 18.5	21 46.9	12 43.7	6 34.6	8 2.3	24 20.7	8 45.7	17 6.7
6 W	21 5 47	17 31 0	4♐44 29	11♐16 7	25 59.1	28 56.9	23 2.2	13 27.0	6 30.0	8 2.0	24 24.1	8 48.0	17 8.1
7 Th	21 9 44	18 31 48	17 43 25	24 6 45	25R 59.8	28 43.5	24 17.4	14 10.3	6 25.6	8 1.9	24 27.6	8 50.2	17 9.4
8 F	21 13 41	19 32 36	0♑26 32	6♑43 6	25 59.2	28D 38.0	25 32.7	14 53.5	6 21.4	8D 1.9	24 31.1	8 52.5	17 10.7
9 Sa	21 17 37	20 33 22	12 56 47	19 7 55	25 56.4	28 40.0	26 47.9	15 36.8	6 17.4	8 2.0	24 34.5	8 54.7	17 12.0
10 Su	21 21 34	21 34 6	25 16 44	1♒23 29	25 51.0	28 49.0	28 3.1	16 20.0	6 13.6	8 2.2	24 38.0	8 57.0	17 13.3
11 M	21 25 30	22 34 50	7♒28 23	13 31 37	25 42.9	29 4.5	29 18.3	17 3.1	6 9.9	8 2.6	24 41.5	8 59.2	17 14.6
12 Tu	21 29 27	23 35 32	19 33 19	25 33 40	25 32.7	29 26.0	0♓33.5	17 46.2	6 6.4	8 3.0	24 45.0	9 1.4	17 15.8
13 W	21 33 23	24 36 13	1♓32 46	7♓30 49	25 20.9	29 53.2	1 48.6	18 29.3	6 3.2	8 3.6	24 48.4	9 3.6	17 16.9
14 Th	21 37 20	25 36 52	13 27 56	19 24 18	25 8.6	0♒25.5	3 3.8	19 12.4	6 0.1	8 4.2	24 51.9	9 5.8	17 18.1
15 F	21 41 16	26 37 30	25 20 10	1♈15 43	24 56.9	1 2.6	4 18.9	19 55.5	5 57.2	8 5.0	24 55.4	9 8.0	17 19.2
16 Sa	21 45 13	27 38 6	7♈11 16	13 7 8	24 46.8	1 44.1	5 34.0	20 38.5	5 54.5	8 5.9	24 58.8	9 10.2	17 20.3
17 Su	21 49 10	28 38 40	19 3 41	25 1 20	24 38.9	2 29.5	6 49.1	21 21.4	5 52.0	8 6.9	25 2.3	9 12.4	17 21.3
18 M	21 53 6	29 39 13	1♉ 0 32	7♉ 1 48	24 33.8	3 18.6	8 4.2	22 4.4	5 49.7	8 8.1	25 5.8	9 14.6	17 22.4
19 Tu	21 57 3	0♓39 44	13 5 41	19 12 45	24 31.1	4 11.2	9 19.3	22 47.3	5 47.6	8 9.3	25 9.2	9 16.8	17 23.3
20 W	22 0 59	1 40 13	25 23 36	1♊38 52	24D 30.4	5 6.8	10 34.3	23 30.2	5 45.7	8 10.7	25 12.7	9 18.9	17 24.3
21 Th	22 4 56	2 40 41	7♊59 10	14 25 5	24 30.8	6 5.4	11 49.3	24 13.0	5 43.9	8 12.1	25 16.1	9 21.0	17 25.2
22 F	22 8 52	3 41 6	20 57 11	27 35 59	24R 30.9	7 6.7	13 4.3	24 55.9	5 42.4	8 13.7	25 19.6	9 23.2	17 26.1
23 Sa	22 12 49	4 41 30	4♋21 52	11♋15 8	24 29.8	8 10.4	14 19.3	25 38.6	5 41.1	8 15.4	25 23.0	9 25.3	17 27.0
24 Su	22 16 45	5 41 52	18 15 55	25 24 11	24 26.5	9 16.5	15 34.3	26 21.4	5 40.0	8 17.2	25 26.5	9 27.4	17 27.8
25 M	22 20 42	6 42 11	2♌39 39	10♌ 1 49	24 20.5	10 24.8	16 49.2	27 4.1	5 39.1	8 19.1	25 29.9	9 29.5	17 28.6
26 Tu	22 24 39	7 42 29	17 29 59	25 3 10	24 11.9	11 35.1	18 4.1	27 46.7	5 38.4	8 21.1	25 33.3	9 31.5	17 29.4
27 W	22 28 35	8 42 45	2♍40 10	10♍19 39	24 1.5	12 47.3	19 19.0	28 29.4	5 37.9	8 23.2	25 36.7	9 33.6	17 30.1
28 Th	22 32 32	9 43 0	18 0 10	25 40 13	23 50.5	14 1.3	20 33.9	29 12.0	5 37.5	8 25.4	25 40.1	9 35.6	17 30.8

Ephemeris reprinted with permission from Astro Communications Services, Inc.

Each planet's retrograde period is shaded gray.

*Giving the positions of planets daily at noon, in LONGITUDE Greenwich Mean Time

Day	Sid.Time	☉	0 hr ☽	Noon ☽	True ☊	☿	♀	♂	♃	♄	♅	♆	♇
1 F	22 36 28	10♓43 12	3♎18 18	10♎53 5	23♊40.2	15♒17.1	21♓48.7	29♈54.5	5♋37.4	8♊27.7	25♒43.5	9♒37.7	17♐31.5
2 Sa	22 40 25	11 43 23	18 23 21	25 48 6	23R 31.7	16 34.5	23 3.5	0♉37.0	5D 37.5	8 30.2	25 46.9	9 39.7	17 32.1
3 Su	22 44 21	12 43 32	3♏ 6 33	10♏18 12	23 25.9	17 53.5	24 18.3	1 19.5	5 37.8	8 32.7	25 50.2	9 41.7	17 32.7
4 M	22 48 18	13 43 40	17 22 44	24 20 4	23 22.6	19 14.1	25 33.1	2 2.0	5 38.2	8 35.3	25 53.6	9 43.6	17 33.3
5 Tu	22 52 14	14 43 47	1♐10 18	7♐53 42	23 21.4	20 36.0	26 47.9	2 44.4	5 38.9	8 38.1	25 56.9	9 45.6	17 33.8
6 W	22 56 11	15 43 52	14 30 37	21 1 30	23 21.3	21 59.4	28 2.6	3 26.8	5 39.7	8 40.9	26 0.3	9 47.5	17 34.3
7 Th	23 0 8	16 43 55	27 26 53	3♑47 18	23 21.1	23 24.2	29 17.3	4 9.1	5 40.8	8 43.9	26 3.6	9 49.5	17 34.7
8 F	23 4 4	17 43 57	10♑ 3 18	16 15 26	23 19.5	24 50.2	0♈32.0	4 51.4	5 42.1	8 46.9	26 6.9	9 51.4	17 35.2
9 Sa	23 8 1	18 43 57	22 24 14	28 30 12	23 15.5	26 17.6	1 46.7	5 33.7	5 43.5	8 50.1	26 10.1	9 53.2	17 35.6
10 Su	23 11 57	19 43 56	4♒33 47	10♒35 24	23 8.5	27 46.3	3 1.3	6 15.9	5 45.1	8 53.3	26 13.4	9 55.1	17 35.9
11 M	23 15 54	20 43 53	16 35 25	22 34 10	22 58.5	29 16.2	4 16.0	6 58.2	5 47.0	8 56.7	26 16.6	9 57.0	17 36.3
12 Tu	23 19 50	21 43 47	28 31 56	4♓28 58	22 46.0	0♓47.3	5 30.6	7 40.3	5 49.0	9 0.1	26 19.9	9 58.8	17 36.6
13 W	23 23 47	22 43 40	10♓25 28	16 21 38	22 31.6	2 19.7	6 45.1	8 22.5	5 51.2	9 3.6	26 23.1	10 0.6	17 36.8
14 Th	23 27 43	23 43 31	22 17 38	28 13 37	22 16.6	3 53.3	7 59.7	9 4.6	5 53.6	9 7.3	26 26.3	10 2.4	17 37.0
15 F	23 31 40	24 43 20	4♈ 9 44	10♈ 6 10	22 2.1	5 28.2	9 14.2	9 46.6	5 56.2	9 11.0	26 29.4	10 4.1	17 37.2
16 Sa	23 35 37	25 43 7	16 3 5	22 0 41	21 49.4	7 4.2	10 28.7	10 28.7	5 59.0	9 14.8	26 32.6	10 5.9	17 37.4
17 Su	23 39 33	26 42 52	27 59 13	3♉58 57	21 39.2	8 41.5	11 43.2	11 10.7	6 2.0	9 18.8	26 35.7	10 7.6	17 37.5
18 M	23 43 30	27 42 35	10♉ 0 11	16 3 18	21 32.1	10 20.0	12 57.6	11 52.6	6 5.1	9 22.8	26 38.8	10 9.3	17 37.6
19 Tu	23 47 26	28 42 16	22 8 41	28 16 48	21 27.9	11 59.7	14 12.0	12 34.6	6 8.4	9 26.9	26 41.9	10 10.9	17 37.6
20 W	23 51 23	29 41 54	4♊28 6	10♊43 8	21 26.1	13 40.7	15 26.4	13 16.5	6 12.0	9 31.1	26 44.9	10 12.6	17R 37.7
21 Th	23 55 19	0♈41 30	17 2 26	23 26 32	21D 25.8	15 22.9	16 40.8	13 58.3	6 15.7	9 35.3	26 48.0	10 14.2	17 37.6
22 F	23 59 16	1 41 4	29 56 0	6♋31 20	21R 25.8	17 6.4	17 55.1	14 40.1	6 19.5	9 39.7	26 51.0	10 15.8	17 37.6
23 Sa	0 3 12	2 40 36	13♋13 0	20 1 24	21 24.9	18 51.1	19 9.4	15 21.9	6 23.6	9 44.2	26 53.9	10 17.4	17 37.5
24 Su	0 7 9	3 40 5	26 56 48	3♌59 21	21 21.9	20 37.2	20 23.6	16 3.6	6 27.8	9 48.7	26 56.9	10 18.9	17 37.4
25 M	0 11 6	4 39 32	11♌ 9 1	18 25 32	21 16.5	22 24.5	21 37.8	16 45.3	6 32.2	9 53.3	26 59.8	10 20.5	17 37.3
26 Tu	0 15 2	5 38 57	25 48 28	3♍17 6	21 8.5	24 13.1	22 52.0	17 27.0	6 36.8	9 58.0	27 2.7	10 22.0	17 37.1
27 W	0 18 59	6 38 19	10♍50 29	18 27 30	20 58.6	26 3.1	24 6.2	18 8.6	6 41.5	10 2.8	27 5.6	10 23.4	17 36.9
28 Th	0 22 55	7 37 39	26 6 50	3♎47 1	20 48.0	27 54.4	25 20.3	18 50.2	6 46.4	10 7.7	27 8.4	10 24.9	17 36.6
29 F	0 26 52	8 36 57	11♎26 36	19 4 7	20 37.8	29 47.0	26 34.4	19 31.7	6 51.5	10 12.7	27 11.3	10 26.3	17 36.3
30 Sa	0 30 48	9 36 13	26 38 11	4♏ 7 35	20 29.4	1♈40.9	27 48.4	20 13.2	6 56.7	10 17.7	27 14.0	10 27.7	17 36.0
31 Su	0 34 45	10 35 28	11♏31 19	18 48 35	20 23.4	3 36.2	29 2.4	20 54.7	7 2.1	10 22.8	27 16.8	10 29.0	17 35.7

LONGITUDE APRIL 2002

Day	Sid.Time	☉	0 hr ☽	Noon ☽	True ☊	☿	♀	♂	♃	♄	♅	♆	♇
1 M	0 38 41	11♈34 40	25♏58 50	3♐ 1 44	20♊20.0	5♈32.8	0♉16.4	21♉36.1	7♋ 7.7	10♊28.0	27♒19.5	10♒30.4	17♐35.3
2 Tu	0 42 38	12 33 51	9♐57 10	16 45 14	20D 18.8	7 30.7	1 30.4	22 17.5	7 13.4	10 33.2	27 22.2	10 31.7	17R 34.9
3 W	0 46 34	13 33 0	23 26 9	0♑ 0 19	20 19.0	9 29.8	2 44.3	22 58.8	7 19.3	10 38.6	27 24.9	10 33.0	17 34.5
4 Th	0 50 31	14 32 7	6♑28 10	12 50 15	20R 19.4	11 30.1	3 58.2	23 40.1	7 25.3	10 44.0	27 27.5	10 34.2	17 34.0
5 F	0 54 28	15 31 13	19 7 9	25 19 28	20 18.9	13 31.6	5 12.0	24 21.4	7 31.5	10 49.5	27 30.1	10 35.5	17 33.5
6 Sa	0 58 24	16 30 16	1♒27 48	7♒32 46	20 16.7	15 34.1	6 25.9	25 2.7	7 37.8	10 55.0	27 32.7	10 36.6	17 33.0
7 Su	1 2 21	17 29 18	13 34 55	19 34 49	20 12.0	17 37.6	7 39.7	25 43.9	7 44.3	11 0.6	27 35.2	10 37.8	17 32.4
8 M	1 6 17	18 28 18	25 32 58	1♓29 50	20 4.8	19 41.9	8 53.4	26 25.0	7 51.0	11 6.3	27 37.7	10 39.0	17 31.8
9 Tu	1 10 14	19 27 17	7♓25 52	13 21 26	19 55.5	21 46.9	10 7.2	27 6.2	7 57.7	11 12.1	27 40.2	10 40.1	17 31.2
10 W	1 14 10	20 26 13	19 16 52	25 12 28	19 44.5	23 52.4	11 20.9	27 47.3	8 4.7	11 17.9	27 42.6	10 41.1	17 30.5
11 Th	1 18 7	21 25 7	1♈ 8 29	7♈ 5 10	19 33.0	25 58.1	12 34.5	28 28.4	8 11.7	11 23.8	27 45.0	10 42.2	17 29.9
12 F	1 22 3	22 24 0	13 2 42	19 1 16	19 21.9	28 3.9	13 48.2	29 9.4	8 19.0	11 29.8	27 47.3	10 43.2	17 29.1
13 Sa	1 26 0	23 22 50	25 1 1	1♉ 2 8	19 12.1	0♉ 9.4	15 1.8	29 50.4	8 26.3	11 35.8	27 49.7	10 44.2	17 28.4
14 Su	1 29 57	24 21 39	7♉ 4 46	13 9 6	19 4.4	2 14.5	16 15.3	0♊31.4	8 33.8	11 41.9	27 51.9	10 45.1	17 27.6
15 M	1 33 53	25 20 25	19 15 18	25 23 36	18 59.2	4 18.7	17 28.8	1 12.3	8 41.4	11 48.0	27 54.2	10 46.1	17 26.8
16 Tu	1 37 50	26 19 10	1♊34 14	7♊47 28	18 56.4	6 21.7	18 42.3	1 53.2	8 49.2	11 54.2	27 56.4	10 47.0	17 26.0
17 W	1 41 46	27 17 52	14 3 37	20 23 0	18D 55.8	8 23.3	19 55.8	2 34.1	8 57.1	12 0.5	27 58.5	10 47.8	17 25.2
18 Th	1 45 43	28 16 32	26 45 59	3♋12 55	18 56.5	10 23.0	21 9.2	3 14.9	9 5.1	12 6.8	28 0.7	10 48.6	17 24.3
19 F	1 49 39	29 15 10	9♋44 12	16 20 12	18 57.6	12 20.6	22 22.5	3 55.7	9 13.3	12 13.2	28 2.7	10 49.4	17 23.4
20 Sa	1 53 36	0♉13 46	23 1 16	29 47 42	18R 58.2	14 15.6	23 35.9	4 36.5	9 21.6	12 19.6	28 4.8	10 50.2	17 22.4
21 Su	1 57 32	1 12 20	6♌39 44	13♌37 31	18 57.5	16 7.9	24 49.2	5 17.2	9 30.0	12 26.1	28 6.8	10 50.9	17 21.5
22 M	2 1 29	2 10 51	20 41 5	27 50 19	18 54.9	17 57.1	26 2.4	5 57.8	9 38.5	12 32.7	28 8.8	10 51.7	17 20.5
23 Tu	2 5 26	3 9 20	5♍ 4 57	12♍24 32	18 50.5	19 43.0	27 15.6	6 38.5	9 47.1	12 39.3	28 10.7	10 52.3	17 19.5
24 W	2 9 22	4 7 47	19 48 27	27 15 52	18 44.6	21 25.3	28 28.7	7 19.1	9 55.9	12 45.9	28 12.5	10 53.0	17 18.4
25 Th	2 13 19	5 6 12	4♎45 52	12♎17 20	18 38.1	23 3.9	29 41.8	7 59.7	10 4.8	12 52.6	28 14.4	10 53.6	17 17.4
26 F	2 17 15	6 4 34	19 49 7	27 19 59	18 31.7	24 38.5	0♊54.9	8 40.2	10 13.8	12 59.4	28 16.2	10 54.1	17 16.3
27 Sa	2 21 12	7 2 55	4♏48 45	12♏14 17	18 26.5	26 9.0	2 7.9	9 20.7	10 22.9	13 6.1	28 17.9	10 54.7	17 15.2
28 Su	2 25 8	8 1 15	19 35 35	26 51 47	18 22.9	27 35.4	3 20.9	10 1.1	10 32.1	13 13.0	28 19.6	10 55.2	17 14.1
29 M	2 29 5	8 59 32	4♐ 2 11	11♐ 6 16	18 21.2	28 57.4	4 33.9	10 41.6	10 41.4	13 19.9	28 21.3	10 55.7	17 12.9
30 Tu	2 33 1	9 57 48	18 3 44	24 54 25	18D 21.1	0♊14.9	5 46.8	11 22.0	10 50.9	13 26.8	28 22.9	10 56.1	17 11.7

*Giving the positions of planets daily at noon, in LONGITUDE Greenwich Mean Time

Noon Ephemeris: GMT*

May 2002

Day	Sid.Time	☉	0 hr ☽	Noon ☽	True ☊	☿	♀	♂	♃	♄	♅	♆	♇
1 W	2 36 58	10♉56 3	1♑38 20	8♑15 40	18♊22.2	1♊27.9	6♊59.6	12♊ 2.3	11♋ 0.4	13♊33.8	28♒24.5	10♒56.5	17♐10.6
2 Th	2 40 55	11 54 16	14 46 41	21 11 46	18 23.8	2 36.3	8 12.4	12 42.7	11 10.1	13 40.8	28 26.0	10 56.9	17R 9.3
3 F	2 44 51	12 52 27	27 31 23	3♒46 3	18 25.1	3 40.1	9 25.2	13 23.0	11 19.8	13 47.8	28 27.5	10 57.2	17 8.1
4 Sa	2 48 48	13 50 37	9♒56 19	16 2 48	18R 25.4	4 39.0	10 37.9	14 3.2	11 29.7	13 54.9	28 29.0	10 57.6	17 6.8
5 Su	2 52 44	14 48 46	22 6 3	28 6 40	18 24.5	5 33.2	11 50.6	14 43.5	11 39.6	14 2.0	28 30.4	10 57.8	17 5.6
6 M	2 56 41	15 46 53	4♓ 5 15	10♓ 2 20	18 22.0	6 22.4	13 3.3	15 23.7	11 49.7	14 9.2	28 31.7	10 58.1	17 4.3
7 Tu	3 0 37	16 44 58	15 58 28	21 54 10	18 18.3	7 6.7	14 15.9	16 3.8	11 59.9	14 16.4	28 33.0	10 58.3	17 3.0
8 W	3 4 34	17 43 3	27 49 52	3♈46 2	18 13.6	7 46.0	15 28.4	16 44.0	12 10.1	14 23.7	28 34.3	10 58.5	17 1.6
9 Th	3 8 30	18 41 5	9♈43 2	15 41 13	18 8.4	8 20.2	16 41.0	17 24.1	12 20.4	14 30.9	28 35.5	10 58.6	17 0.3
10 F	3 12 27	19 39 7	21 40 54	27 42 22	18 3.3	8 49.4	17 53.4	18 4.2	12 30.9	14 38.2	28 36.6	10 58.7	16 58.9
11 Sa	3 16 24	20 37 6	3♉45 51	9♉51 33	17 58.9	9 13.5	19 5.9	18 44.2	12 41.4	14 45.6	28 37.8	10 58.8	16 57.5
12 Su	3 20 20	21 35 5	15 59 37	22 10 14	17 55.7	9 32.4	20 18.3	19 24.2	12 52.0	14 53.0	28 38.8	10 58.9	16 56.1
13 M	3 24 17	22 33 2	28 23 31	4♊39 36	17 53.7	9 46.3	21 30.6	20 4.2	13 2.7	15 0.4	28 39.8	10R 58.9	16 54.7
14 Tu	3 28 13	23 30 57	10♊58 33	17 20 31	17D 53.0	9 55.1	22 42.9	20 44.2	13 13.5	15 7.8	28 40.8	10 58.9	16 53.3
15 W	3 32 10	24 28 51	23 45 35	0♋13 52	17 53.5	9R 59.0	23 55.1	21 24.1	13 24.4	15 15.2	28 41.7	10 58.8	16 51.8
16 Th	3 36 6	25 26 43	6♋45 28	13 20 30	17 54.7	9 57.9	25 7.3	22 4.0	13 35.3	15 22.7	28 42.6	10 58.7	16 50.4
17 F	3 40 3	26 24 33	19 59 4	26 41 18	17 56.2	9 52.2	26 19.5	22 43.9	13 46.4	15 30.3	28 43.5	10 58.6	16 48.9
18 Sa	3 43 59	27 22 22	3♌27 16	10♌17 4	17 57.4	9 41.9	27 31.6	23 23.7	13 57.5	15 37.8	28 44.2	10 58.5	16 47.4
19 Su	3 47 56	28 20 9	17 10 42	24 8 11	17R 58.1	9 27.4	28 43.6	24 3.6	14 8.7	15 45.3	28 45.0	10 58.3	16 45.9
20 M	3 51 53	29 17 54	1♍ 9 26	8♍14 20	17 57.9	9 8.8	29 55.6	24 43.3	14 19.9	15 52.9	28 45.7	10 58.1	16 44.4
21 Tu	3 55 49	0♊15 37	15 22 37	22 34 0	17 56.9	8 46.6	1♋ 7.5	25 23.1	14 31.3	16 0.5	28 46.3	10 57.8	16 42.9
22 W	3 59 46	1 13 19	29 48 4	7♎ 4 17	17 55.3	8 21.2	2 19.4	26 2.8	14 42.7	16 8.1	28 46.9	10 57.6	16 41.4
23 Th	4 3 42	2 11 0	14♎22 4	21 40 44	17 53.4	7 53.0	3 31.2	26 42.5	14 54.2	16 15.8	28 47.4	10 57.3	16 39.8
24 F	4 7 39	3 8 39	28 59 32	6♏17 41	17 51.5	7 22.6	4 43.0	27 22.1	15 5.7	16 23.4	28 47.9	10 56.9	16 38.3
25 Sa	4 11 35	4 6 16	13♏34 23	20 48 51	17 50.0	6 50.4	5 54.6	28 1.7	15 17.3	16 31.1	28 48.3	10 56.6	16 36.7
26 Su	4 15 32	5 3 52	28 0 19	5♐ 8 6	17 49.1	6 17.0	7 6.3	28 41.3	15 29.0	16 38.8	28 48.7	10 56.2	16 35.2
27 M	4 19 28	6 1 27	12♐11 37	19 10 21	17D 48.9	5 43.0	8 17.9	29 20.9	15 40.8	16 46.5	28 49.1	10 55.7	16 33.6
28 Tu	4 23 25	6 59 1	26 3 55	2♑52 3	17 49.2	5 9.1	9 29.4	0♋ 0.4	15 52.6	16 54.2	28 49.4	10 55.3	16 32.0
29 W	4 27 22	7 56 35	9♑34 36	16 11 32	17 49.9	4 35.8	10 40.8	0 40.0	16 4.5	17 1.9	28 49.6	10 54.8	16 30.4
30 Th	4 31 18	8 54 7	22 42 57	29 9 1	17 50.8	4 3.6	11 52.2	1 19.4	16 16.4	17 9.7	28 49.8	10 54.3	16 28.8
31 F	4 35 15	9 51 38	5♒29 59	11♒46 14	17 51.6	3 33.1	13 3.6	1 58.9	16 28.4	17 17.4	28 50.0	10 53.7	16 27.3

Longitude

June 2002

Day	Sid.Time	☉	0 hr ☽	Noon ☽	True ☊	☿	♀	♂	♃	♄	♅	♆	♇
1 Sa	4 39 11	10♊49 8	17♒58 10	24♒ 6 14	17♊52.2	3♊ 4.9	14♋14.9	2♋38.3	16♋40.5	17♊25.2	28♒50.1	10♒53.1	16♐25.7
2 Su	4 43 8	11 46 37	0♓10 57	6♓12 52	17 52.4	2R 39.3	15 26.1	3 17.7	16 52.6	17 33.0	28 50.1	10R 52.5	16R 24.1
3 M	4 47 4	12 44 6	12 12 32	18 10 30	17R 52.5	2 16.9	16 37.2	3 57.1	17 4.7	17 40.7	28R 50.1	10 51.9	16 22.5
4 Tu	4 51 1	13 41 34	24 7 23	0♈ 3 43	17 52.2	1 57.8	17 48.3	4 36.5	17 17.0	17 48.5	28 50.1	10 51.2	16 20.8
5 W	4 54 57	14 39 1	6♈ 0 5	11 57 0	17 51.9	1 42.5	18 59.4	5 15.8	17 29.2	17 56.3	28 50.0	10 50.5	16 19.2
6 Th	4 58 54	15 36 28	17 55 0	23 54 34	17 51.6	1 31.2	20 10.3	5 55.1	17 41.6	18 4.1	28 49.8	10 49.8	16 17.6
7 F	5 2 51	16 33 54	29 56 9	6♉ 0 10	17 51.4	1 24.1	21 21.2	6 34.4	17 54.0	18 11.9	28 49.6	10 49.0	16 16.0
8 Sa	5 6 47	17 31 19	12♉ 7 0	18 16 56	17D 51.3	1D 21.3	22 32.1	7 13.7	18 6.4	18 19.7	28 49.4	10 48.2	16 14.4
9 Su	5 10 44	18 28 44	24 30 17	0♊47 13	17 51.3	1 22.9	23 42.9	7 52.9	18 18.9	18 27.5	28 49.1	10 47.4	16 12.8
10 M	5 14 40	19 26 8	7♊ 7 56	13 32 32	17R 51.4	1 29.1	24 53.6	8 32.1	18 31.4	18 35.3	28 48.8	10 46.6	16 11.2
11 Tu	5 18 37	20 23 31	20 1 3	26 33 30	17 51.4	1 39.7	26 4.2	9 11.3	18 44.0	18 43.1	28 48.4	10 45.7	16 9.6
12 W	5 22 33	21 20 53	3♋ 9 49	9♋49 54	17 51.2	1 54.9	27 14.8	9 50.5	18 56.6	18 50.9	28 47.9	10 44.8	16 8.0
13 Th	5 26 30	22 18 15	16 33 37	23 20 47	17 50.8	2 14.6	28 25.3	10 29.7	19 9.3	18 58.7	28 47.5	10 43.9	16 6.4
14 F	5 30 26	23 15 36	0♌11 10	7♌ 4 34	17 50.3	2 38.7	29 35.7	11 8.8	19 22.0	19 6.5	28 46.9	10 43.0	16 4.8
15 Sa	5 34 23	24 12 56	14 0 42	20 59 19	17 49.6	3 7.3	0♌46.0	11 47.9	19 34.7	19 14.3	28 46.4	10 42.0	16 3.2
16 Su	5 38 20	25 10 14	28 0 7	5♍ 2 49	17 49.0	3 40.2	1 56.3	12 27.0	19 47.5	19 22.1	28 45.7	10 41.0	16 1.6
17 M	5 42 16	26 7 32	12♍ 7 8	19 12 46	17 48.7	4 17.5	3 6.5	13 6.0	20 0.3	19 29.8	28 45.1	10 40.0	16 0.0
18 Tu	5 46 13	27 4 50	26 19 24	3♎26 43	17D 48.7	4 58.9	4 16.6	13 45.1	20 13.2	19 37.6	28 44.4	10 38.9	15 58.5
19 W	5 50 9	28 2 6	10♎34 25	17 42 11	17 49.1	5 44.5	5 26.6	14 24.1	20 26.1	19 45.4	28 43.6	10 37.8	15 56.9
20 Th	5 54 6	28 59 21	24 49 39	1♏56 28	17 49.8	6 34.1	6 36.5	15 3.1	20 39.0	19 53.1	28 42.8	10 36.7	15 55.3
21 F	5 58 2	29 56 36	9♏ 2 17	16 6 43	17 50.8	7 27.8	7 46.3	15 42.0	20 52.0	20 0.8	28 41.9	10 35.6	15 53.8
22 Sa	6 1 59	0♋53 50	23 9 24	0♐ 9 56	17 51.6	8 25.3	8 56.1	16 21.0	21 4.9	20 8.5	28 41.1	10 34.5	15 52.2
23 Su	6 5 55	1 51 4	7♐ 7 57	14 3 5	17R 52.1	9 26.8	10 5.7	16 59.9	21 18.0	20 16.2	28 40.1	10 33.3	15 50.7
24 M	6 9 52	2 48 17	20 54 59	27 43 21	17 51.9	10 32.1	11 15.3	17 38.8	21 31.0	20 23.9	28 39.1	10 32.1	15 49.2
25 Tu	6 13 49	3 45 30	4♑27 54	11♑ 8 26	17 51.0	11 41.2	12 24.7	18 17.7	21 44.1	20 31.6	28 38.1	10 30.9	15 47.7
26 W	6 17 45	4 42 43	17 44 45	24 16 46	17 49.3	12 54.0	13 34.1	18 56.5	21 57.2	20 39.3	28 37.1	10 29.7	15 46.2
27 Th	6 21 42	5 39 55	0♒44 27	7♒ 7 49	17 46.9	14 10.4	14 43.3	19 35.4	22 10.3	20 46.9	28 35.9	10 28.5	15 44.7
28 F	6 25 38	6 37 8	13 27 0	19 42 10	17 44.2	15 30.5	15 52.5	20 14.2	22 23.5	20 54.5	28 34.8	10 27.2	15 43.2
29 Sa	6 29 35	7 34 20	25 53 34	2♓ 1 29	17 41.5	16 54.2	17 1.6	20 53.0	22 36.6	21 2.1	28 33.6	10 25.9	15 41.7
30 Su	6 33 31	8 31 32	8♓ 6 19	14 8 28	17 39.1	18 21.4	18 10.5	21 31.8	22 49.8	21 9.7	28 32.4	10 24.6	15 40.3

*Giving the positions of planets daily at noon,
in LONGITUDE Greenwich Mean Time

NOON EPHEMERIS: GMT* — JULY 2002

Day	Sid.Time	☉	0 hr ☽	Noon ☽	True ☊	☿	♀	♂	♃	♄	♅	♆	♇
1 M	6 37 28	9♋28 44	20♓ 8 23	26♓ 6 37	17♊37.5	19♊52.1	19♌19.4	22♋10.5	23♋ 3.0	21♊17.3	28♒31.1	10♒23.3	15♐38.8
2 Tu	6 41 25	10 25 57	2♈ 3 40	8♈ 0 7	17D 36.8	21 26.3	20 28.1	22 49.3	23 16.3	21 24.8	28R 29.8	10R 22.0	15R 37.4
3 W	6 45 21	11 23 9	13 56 33	19 53 32	17 37.1	23 3.9	21 36.8	23 28.0	23 29.5	21 32.3	28 28.4	10 20.6	15 36.0
4 Th	6 49 18	12 20 22	25 51 42	1♉51 36	17 38.1	24 44.8	22 45.3	24 6.7	23 42.8	21 39.8	28 27.0	10 19.2	15 34.6
5 F	6 53 14	13 17 35	7♉53 51	13 58 58	17 39.7	26 28.9	23 53.7	24 45.4	23 56.1	21 47.3	28 25.6	10 17.8	15 33.2
6 Sa	6 57 11	14 14 48	20 7 30	26 19 55	17 41.3	28 16.2	25 2.0	25 24.1	24 9.4	21 54.7	28 24.1	10 16.4	15 31.9
7 Su	7 1 7	15 12 2	2♊36 38	8♊58 0	17 42.4	0♋ 6.5	26 10.2	26 2.8	24 22.7	22 2.1	28 22.6	10 15.0	15 30.5
8 M	7 5 4	16 9 16	15 24 20	21 55 48	17R 42.6	1 59.6	27 18.3	26 41.5	24 36.1	22 9.5	28 21.1	10 13.5	15 29.2
9 Tu	7 9 0	17 6 30	28 32 30	5♋14 27	17 41.5	3 55.5	28 26.3	27 20.1	24 49.4	22 16.8	28 19.5	10 12.1	15 27.9
10 W	7 12 57	18 3 44	12♋ 1 31	18 53 28	17 39.1	5 53.8	29 34.1	27 58.7	25 2.8	22 24.2	28 17.9	10 10.6	15 26.6
11 Th	7 16 54	19 0 59	25 49 59	2♌50 37	17 35.3	7 54.5	0♍41.9	28 37.3	25 16.2	22 31.5	28 16.2	10 9.1	15 25.3
12 F	7 20 50	19 58 13	9♌54 51	17 2 6	17 30.7	9 57.1	1 49.4	29 15.9	25 29.5	22 38.7	28 14.5	10 7.6	15 24.0
13 Sa	7 24 47	20 55 28	24 11 41	1♍22 58	17 25.9	12 1.5	2 56.9	29 54.5	25 42.9	22 45.9	28 12.8	10 6.1	15 22.8
14 Su	7 28 43	21 52 43	8♍35 15	15 47 54	17 21.6	14 7.3	4 4.2	0♌33.1	25 56.3	22 53.1	28 11.0	10 4.6	15 21.6
15 M	7 32 40	22 49 57	23 0 17	0♎11 51	17 18.4	16 14.2	5 11.4	1 11.6	26 9.7	23 0.3	28 9.2	10 3.1	15 20.4
16 Tu	7 36 36	23 47 12	7♎22 7	14 30 40	17 16.6	18 22.0	6 18.4	1 50.2	26 23.1	23 7.4	28 7.4	10 1.5	15 19.2
17 W	7 40 33	24 44 27	21 37 12	28 41 26	17D 16.3	20 30.4	7 25.3	2 28.7	26 36.5	23 14.4	28 5.6	9 60.0	15 18.1
18 Th	7 44 29	25 41 42	5♏43 11	12♏42 20	17 17.2	22 38.9	8 32.0	3 7.2	26 49.9	23 21.4	28 3.7	9 58.4	15 17.0
19 F	7 48 26	26 38 57	19 38 47	26 32 28	17 18.6	24 47.4	9 38.5	3 45.7	27 3.3	23 28.4	28 1.8	9 56.8	15 15.8
20 Sa	7 52 23	27 36 12	3♐23 22	10♐11 27	17 19.6	26 55.6	10 44.9	4 24.2	27 16.7	23 35.4	27 59.8	9 55.3	15 14.8
21 Su	7 56 19	28 33 28	16 56 40	23 39 1	17R 19.7	29 3.3	11 51.2	5 2.6	27 30.1	23 42.3	27 57.9	9 53.7	15 13.7
22 M	8 0 16	29 30 44	0♑18 26	6♑54 53	17 18.0	1♌10.2	12 57.2	5 41.1	27 43.5	23 49.1	27 55.9	9 52.1	15 12.7
23 Tu	8 4 12	0♌28 0	13 28 18	19 58 38	17 14.4	3 16.1	14 3.1	6 19.5	27 56.9	23 56.0	27 53.9	9 50.5	15 11.7
24 W	8 8 9	1 25 17	26 25 50	2♒49 51	17 8.7	5 21.0	15 8.8	6 57.9	28 10.3	24 2.7	27 51.8	9 48.9	15 10.7
25 Th	8 12 5	2 22 35	9♒10 40	15 28 16	17 1.5	7 24.6	16 14.3	7 36.4	28 23.6	24 9.4	27 49.8	9 47.3	15 9.7
26 F	8 16 2	3 19 53	21 42 43	27 54 4	16 53.4	9 26.8	17 19.6	8 14.8	28 37.0	24 16.1	27 47.7	9 45.7	15 8.8
27 Sa	8 19 58	4 17 12	4♓ 2 28	10♓ 8 5	16 45.0	11 27.6	18 24.8	8 53.1	28 50.4	24 22.7	27 45.6	9 44.1	15 7.9
28 Su	8 23 55	5 14 31	16 11 9	22 11 58	16 37.4	13 27.0	19 29.7	9 31.5	29 3.7	24 29.3	27 43.4	9 42.4	15 7.0
29 M	8 27 52	6 11 52	28 10 51	4♈ 8 14	16 31.1	15 24.8	20 34.5	10 9.9	29 17.1	24 35.8	27 41.3	9 40.8	15 6.1
30 Tu	8 31 48	7 9 14	10♈ 4 32	16 0 16	16 26.6	17 21.0	21 39.0	10 48.2	29 30.4	24 42.3	27 39.1	9 39.2	15 5.3
31 W	8 35 45	8 6 36	21 55 56	27 52 9	16 24.2	19 15.6	22 43.3	11 26.6	29 43.7	24 48.7	27 36.9	9 37.5	15 4.5

LONGITUDE — AUGUST 2002

Day	Sid.Time	☉	0 hr ☽	Noon ☽	True ☊	☿	♀	♂	♃	♄	♅	♆	♇
1 Th	8 39 41	9♌ 4 0	3♉49 29	9♉48 35	16♊23.5	21♌ 8.6	23♍47.5	12♌ 4.9	29♋57.0	24♊55.1	27♒34.7	9♒35.9	15♐ 3.7
2 F	8 43 38	10 1 25	15 50 4	21 54 35	16D 24.1	22 59.9	24 51.4	12 43.3	0♌10.3	25 1.4	27R 32.4	9R 34.3	15R 3.0
3 Sa	8 47 34	10 58 51	28 2 46	4♊15 13	16 25.1	24 49.7	25 55.0	13 21.6	0 23.6	25 7.6	27 30.2	9 32.6	15 2.2
4 Su	8 51 31	11 56 19	10♊32 32	16 55 13	16R 25.6	26 37.8	26 58.5	13 59.9	0 36.9	25 13.8	27 27.9	9 31.0	15 1.5
5 M	8 55 27	12 53 47	23 23 44	29 58 26	16 24.7	28 24.3	28 1.7	14 38.3	0 50.1	25 20.0	27 25.6	9 29.4	15 0.9
6 Tu	8 59 24	13 51 17	6♋39 33	13♋27 13	16 21.8	0♍ 9.3	29 4.7	15 16.6	1 3.3	25 26.1	27 23.3	9 27.8	15 0.3
7 W	9 3 21	14 48 48	20 21 22	27 21 49	16 16.6	1 52.6	0♎ 7.4	15 54.9	1 16.5	25 32.1	27 21.0	9 26.1	14 59.6
8 Th	9 7 17	15 46 20	4♌28 11	11♌39 53	16 9.2	3 34.3	1 9.9	16 33.2	1 29.7	25 38.0	27 18.7	9 24.5	14 59.1
9 F	9 11 14	16 43 53	18 56 13	26 16 19	16 0.4	5 14.5	2 12.1	17 11.5	1 42.9	25 43.9	27 16.4	9 22.9	14 58.5
10 Sa	9 15 10	17 41 27	3♍39 13	11♍ 3 50	15 51.1	6 53.1	3 14.0	17 49.7	1 56.0	25 49.7	27 14.0	9 21.3	14 58.0
11 Su	9 19 7	18 39 2	18 29 7	25 54 1	15 42.4	8 30.1	4 15.7	18 28.0	2 9.1	25 55.5	27 11.7	9 19.7	14 57.5
12 M	9 23 3	19 36 38	3♎17 32	10♎38 46	15 35.5	10 5.6	5 17.0	19 6.3	2 22.2	26 1.2	27 9.3	9 18.1	14 57.1
13 Tu	9 27 0	20 34 14	17 56 59	25 11 34	15 30.8	11 39.5	6 18.1	19 44.5	2 35.2	26 6.8	27 6.9	9 16.5	14 56.6
14 W	9 30 56	21 31 52	2♏22 4	9♏28 11	15 28.4	13 11.9	7 18.8	20 22.8	2 48.2	26 12.4	27 4.5	9 14.9	14 56.2
15 Th	9 34 53	22 29 31	16 29 45	23 26 43	15D 27.9	14 42.7	8 19.2	21 1.0	3 1.2	26 17.9	27 2.2	9 13.3	14 55.9
16 F	9 38 50	23 27 11	0♐19 10	7♐ 7 13	15 28.2	16 11.9	9 19.3	21 39.2	3 14.2	26 23.3	26 59.8	9 11.7	14 55.5
17 Sa	9 42 46	24 24 51	13 51 4	20 30 56	15R 28.3	17 39.6	10 19.1	22 17.5	3 27.1	26 28.6	26 57.4	9 10.2	14 55.2
18 Su	9 46 43	25 22 33	27 7 3	3♑39 40	15 26.9	19 5.6	11 18.4	22 55.7	3 40.0	26 33.9	26 55.0	9 8.6	14 55.0
19 M	9 50 39	26 20 16	10♑ 9 0	16 35 14	15 23.3	20 30.1	12 17.5	23 33.9	3 52.8	26 39.1	26 52.6	9 7.1	14 54.7
20 Tu	9 54 36	27 18 0	22 58 35	29 19 11	15 17.0	21 52.9	13 16.1	24 12.1	4 5.6	26 44.2	26 50.2	9 5.5	14 54.5
21 W	9 58 32	28 15 45	5♒37 9	11♒52 35	15 7.9	23 14.0	14 14.3	24 50.3	4 18.4	26 49.3	26 47.8	9 4.0	14 54.4
22 Th	10 2 29	29 13 31	18 5 36	24 16 14	14 56.5	24 33.4	15 12.1	25 28.5	4 31.1	26 54.2	26 45.4	9 2.5	14 54.2
23 F	10 6 25	0♍11 19	0♓24 35	6♓30 43	14 43.7	25 51.1	16 9.5	26 6.7	4 43.8	26 59.1	26 43.0	9 1.0	14 54.1
24 Sa	10 10 22	1 9 8	12 34 44	18 36 46	14 30.6	27 6.9	17 6.5	26 44.9	4 56.5	27 4.0	26 40.7	8 59.5	14 54.0
25 Su	10 14 19	2 6 59	24 36 57	0♈35 29	14 18.2	28 20.9	18 3.0	27 23.1	5 9.1	27 8.7	26 38.3	8 58.0	14 54.0
26 M	10 18 15	3 4 51	6♈32 37	12 28 37	14 7.5	29 33.0	18 59.1	28 1.3	5 21.6	27 13.3	26 35.9	8 56.6	14D 54.0
27 Tu	10 22 12	4 2 45	18 23 50	24 18 39	13 59.3	0♎43.0	19 54.6	28 39.4	5 34.1	27 17.9	26 33.5	8 55.1	14 54.0
28 W	10 26 8	5 0 41	0♉13 30	6♉ 8 53	13 53.8	1 50.9	20 49.7	29 17.6	5 46.6	27 22.4	26 31.2	8 53.7	14 54.0
29 Th	10 30 5	5 58 39	12 5 19	18 3 24	13 50.8	2 56.7	21 44.3	29 55.8	5 59.0	27 26.8	26 28.8	8 52.3	14 54.1
30 F	10 34 1	6 56 38	24 3 43	0♊ 6 55	13 49.8	4 0.2	22 38.3	0♍34.0	6 11.4	27 31.2	26 26.5	8 50.9	14 54.2
31 Sa	10 37 58	7 54 40	6♊13 41	12 24 38	13 49.7	5 1.2	23 31.9	1 12.2	6 23.7	27 35.4	26 24.1	8 49.5	14 54.4

*Giving the positions of planets daily at noon, in LONGITUDE Greenwich Mean Time

Noon Ephemeris: GMT* September 2002

Day	Sid.Time	☉	0 hr ☽	Noon ☽	True ☊	☿	♀	♂	♃	♄	♅	♆	♇
1 Su	10 41 54	8♍52 43	18♊40 28	25♊ 1 48	13♊49.4	5♎59.7	24♎24.8	1♍50.3	6♌36.0	27♊39.6	26♒21.8	8♒48.1	14♐54.6
2 M	10 45 51	9 50 48	1♋29 11	8♋ 3 10	13R 47.9	6 55.4	25 17.2	2 28.5	6 48.2	27 43.6	26R 19.5	8R 46.8	14 54.8
3 Tu	10 49 48	10 48 55	14 44 8	21 32 24	13 44.2	7 48.3	26 8.9	3 6.7	7 0.4	27 47.6	26 17.2	8 45.5	14 55.0
4 W	10 53 44	11 47 5	28 28 4	5♌31 5	13 37.9	8 38.2	27 0.1	3 44.9	7 12.5	27 51.5	26 14.9	8 44.2	14 55.3
5 Th	10 57 41	12 45 15	12♌41 12	19 57 57	13 29.1	9 24.8	27 50.6	4 23.0	7 24.5	27 55.3	26 12.6	8 42.9	14 55.6
6 F	11 1 37	13 43 28	27 20 36	4♍48 15	13 18.5	10 7.8	28 40.4	5 1.2	7 36.5	27 59.0	26 10.4	8 41.6	14 56.0
7 Sa	11 5 34	14 41 43	12♍19 48	19 54 0	13 7.2	10 47.2	29 29.5	5 39.4	7 48.4	28 2.6	26 8.1	8 40.4	14 56.4
8 Su	11 9 30	15 39 59	27 29 30	5♎ 4 57	12 56.5	11 22.6	0♏17.9	6 17.6	8 0.3	28 6.1	26 5.9	8 39.1	14 56.8
9 M	11 13 27	16 38 16	12♎39 2	20 10 30	12 47.8	11 53.7	1 5.5	6 55.7	8 12.1	28 9.5	26 3.7	8 37.9	14 57.2
10 Tu	11 17 23	17 36 36	27 38 17	5♏ 1 29	12 41.6	12 20.3	1 52.3	7 33.9	8 23.8	28 12.9	26 1.5	8 36.7	14 57.7
11 W	11 21 20	18 34 57	12♏19 26	19 31 37	12 38.1	12 41.9	2 38.3	8 12.1	8 35.5	28 16.1	25 59.4	8 35.6	14 58.2
12 Th	11 25 17	19 33 19	26 37 47	3♐37 48	12 36.7	12 58.4	3 23.5	8 50.3	8 47.1	28 19.2	25 57.2	8 34.4	14 58.8
13 F	11 29 13	20 31 44	10♐31 44	17 19 44	12 36.6	13 9.3	4 7.8	9 28.4	8 58.6	28 22.3	25 55.1	8 33.3	14 59.3
14 Sa	11 33 10	21 30 9	24 2 7	0♑39 11	12 36.4	13R 14.3	4 51.1	10 6.6	9 10.1	28 25.2	25 53.0	8 32.2	14 60.0
15 Su	11 37 6	22 28 37	7♑11 20	13 38 59	12 35.0	13 13.2	5 33.4	10 44.8	9 21.4	28 28.1	25 51.0	8 31.2	15 0.6
16 M	11 41 3	23 27 5	20 2 32	26 22 23	12 31.2	13 5.5	6 14.8	11 22.9	9 32.8	28 30.8	25 48.9	8 30.1	15 1.3
17 Tu	11 44 59	24 25 36	2♒38 54	8♒52 28	12 24.8	12 51.1	6 55.1	12 1.1	9 44.0	28 33.5	25 46.9	8 29.1	15 2.0
18 W	11 48 56	25 24 8	15 3 22	21 11 53	12 15.5	12 29.8	7 34.2	12 39.3	9 55.1	28 36.0	25 44.9	8 28.1	15 2.7
19 Th	11 52 52	26 22 42	27 18 17	3♓22 46	12 3.9	12 1.5	8 12.3	13 17.4	10 6.2	28 38.4	25 43.0	8 27.1	15 3.5
20 F	11 56 49	27 21 18	9♓25 31	15 26 42	11 50.9	11 26.2	8 49.2	13 55.6	10 17.2	28 40.8	25 41.0	8 26.2	15 4.3
21 Sa	12 0 46	28 19 55	21 26 29	27 25 1	11 37.4	10 44.1	9 24.8	14 33.8	10 28.1	28 43.0	25 39.1	8 25.3	15 5.1
22 Su	12 4 42	29 18 35	3♈22 26	9♈18 56	11 24.7	9 55.7	9 59.1	15 11.9	10 38.9	28 45.1	25 37.3	8 24.4	15 6.0
23 M	12 8 39	0♎17 16	15 14 40	21 9 52	11 13.7	9 1.4	10 32.2	15 50.1	10 49.7	28 47.1	25 35.4	8 23.5	15 6.9
24 Tu	12 12 35	1 15 59	27 4 45	2♉59 39	11 5.1	8 2.2	11 3.8	16 28.3	11 0.3	28 49.1	25 33.6	8 22.7	15 7.8
25 W	12 16 32	2 14 45	8♉54 50	14 50 43	10 59.4	6 59.0	11 34.0	17 6.5	11 10.9	28 50.9	25 31.8	8 21.9	15 8.8
26 Th	12 20 28	3 13 33	20 47 41	26 46 13	10 56.2	5 53.3	12 2.7	17 44.6	11 21.3	28 52.6	25 30.1	8 21.1	15 9.7
27 F	12 24 25	4 12 23	2♊46 49	8♊50 1	10D 55.2	4 46.6	12 29.9	18 22.8	11 31.7	28 54.2	25 28.4	8 20.4	15 10.8
28 Sa	12 28 21	5 11 15	14 56 24	21 6 34	10 55.5	3 40.4	12 55.5	19 1.0	11 42.0	28 55.7	25 26.7	8 19.6	15 11.8
29 Su	12 32 18	6 10 10	27 21 8	3♋40 43	10R 56.0	2 36.5	13 19.4	19 39.2	11 52.2	28 57.1	25 25.1	8 19.0	15 12.9
30 M	12 36 14	7 9 7	10♋ 5 55	16 37 17	10 55.6	1 36.6	13 41.7	20 17.4	12 2.3	28 58.4	25 23.5	8 18.3	15 14.0

Longitude October 2002

Day	Sid.Time	☉	0 hr ☽	Noon ☽	True ☊	☿	♀	♂	♃	♄	♅	♆	♇
1 Tu	12 40 11	8♎ 8 6	23♋15 18	0♌ 0 23	10♊53.5	0♎42.4	14♏ 2.1	20♍55.6	12♌12.3	28♊59.5	25♒21.9	8♒17.7	15♐15.1
2 W	12 44 8	9 7 8	6♌52 48	13 52 42	10R 49.1	29♍55.4	14 20.7	21 33.9	12 22.2	29 0.6	25R 20.4	8R 17.1	15 16.3
3 Th	12 48 4	10 6 12	21 0 0	28 14 26	10 42.5	29R 16.7	14 37.5	22 12.1	12 32.0	29 1.5	25 18.9	8 16.5	15 17.5
4 F	12 52 1	11 5 18	5♍35 32	13♍ 2 34	10 34.2	28 47.5	14 52.2	22 50.3	12 41.7	29 2.4	25 17.4	8 16.0	15 18.7
5 Sa	12 55 57	12 4 26	20 34 35	28 10 25	10 25.1	28 28.4	15 5.0	23 28.5	12 51.3	29 3.1	25 16.0	8 15.5	15 20.0
6 Su	12 59 54	13 3 36	5♎48 48	13♎28 18	10 16.4	28D 19.7	15 15.7	24 6.8	13 0.8	29 3.7	25 14.6	8 15.0	15 21.3
7 M	13 3 50	14 2 48	21 7 30	28 45 0	10 9.3	28 21.7	15 24.2	24 45.0	13 10.2	29 4.2	25 13.3	8 14.5	15 22.6
8 Tu	13 7 47	15 2 3	6♏19 28	13♏49 46	10 4.3	28 34.3	15 30.6	25 23.2	13 19.4	29 4.6	25 12.0	8 14.1	15 23.9
9 W	13 11 43	16 1 19	21 14 54	28 34 9	10 1.7	28 57.1	15 34.7	26 1.5	13 28.6	29 4.9	25 10.8	8 13.7	15 25.3
10 Th	13 15 40	17 0 37	5♐46 56	12♐52 57	10D 1.2	29 29.6	15R 36.5	26 39.7	13 37.6	29 5.1	25 9.5	8 13.4	15 26.7
11 F	13 19 37	17 59 57	19 52 4	26 44 19	10 2.0	0♎11.3	15 36.0	27 18.0	13 46.5	29R 5.1	25 8.4	8 13.1	15 28.1
12 Sa	13 23 33	18 59 18	3♑29 53	10♑ 9 4	10 3.0	1 1.4	15 33.0	27 56.2	13 55.3	29 5.1	25 7.3	8 12.8	15 29.6
13 Su	13 27 30	19 58 42	16 42 15	23 9 52	10R 3.2	1 59.2	15 27.7	28 34.5	14 4.0	29 4.9	25 6.2	8 12.5	15 31.0
14 M	13 31 26	20 58 7	29 32 24	5♒50 22	10 1.9	3 3.9	15 20.0	29 12.7	14 12.6	29 4.6	25 5.2	8 12.3	15 32.6
15 Tu	13 35 23	21 57 34	12♒ 4 16	18 14 35	9 58.6	4 14.6	15 9.8	29 51.0	14 21.0	29 4.2	25 4.2	8 12.1	15 34.1
16 W	13 39 19	22 57 2	24 21 47	0♓26 19	9 53.2	5 30.7	14 57.2	0♎29.3	14 29.3	29 3.8	25 3.2	8 12.0	15 35.6
17 Th	13 43 16	23 56 32	6♓28 37	12 29 4	9 46.0	6 51.5	14 42.2	1 7.5	14 37.5	29 3.1	25 2.4	8 11.9	15 37.2
18 F	13 47 12	24 56 5	18 27 59	24 25 42	9 37.7	8 16.2	14 24.8	1 45.8	14 45.5	29 2.4	25 1.5	8 11.8	15 38.8
19 Sa	13 51 9	25 55 39	0♈22 31	6♈18 39	9 29.0	9 44.2	14 5.1	2 24.1	14 53.4	29 1.6	25 0.7	8 11.7	15 40.4
20 Su	13 55 6	26 55 15	12 14 23	18 9 54	9 20.8	11 15.1	13 43.2	3 2.3	15 1.2	29 0.7	24 60.0	8D 11.7	15 42.1
21 M	13 59 2	27 54 52	24 5 25	0♉ 1 9	9 13.7	12 48.2	13 19.1	3 40.6	15 8.9	28 59.6	24 59.2	8 11.7	15 43.8
22 Tu	14 2 59	28 54 32	5♉57 19	11 54 7	9 8.5	14 23.2	12 53.0	4 18.9	15 16.4	28 58.5	24 58.6	8 11.8	15 45.5
23 W	14 6 55	29 54 14	17 51 47	23 50 36	9 5.2	15 59.8	12 24.9	4 57.2	15 23.8	28 57.2	24 58.0	8 11.9	15 47.2
24 Th	14 10 52	0♏53 59	29 50 50	5♊52 49	9D 3.9	17 37.5	11 55.1	5 35.5	15 31.0	28 55.8	24 57.4	8 12.0	15 48.9
25 F	14 14 48	1 53 45	11♊56 52	18 3 22	9 4.3	19 16.0	11 23.8	6 13.9	15 38.1	28 54.3	24 56.9	8 12.1	15 50.7
26 Sa	14 18 45	2 53 33	24 12 44	0♋25 24	9 5.6	20 55.3	10 51.0	6 52.2	15 45.1	28 52.8	24 56.4	8 12.3	15 52.5
27 Su	14 22 41	3 53 24	6♋41 49	13 2 26	9 7.3	22 35.0	10 17.0	7 30.5	15 51.9	28 51.1	24 56.0	8 12.5	15 54.3
28 M	14 26 38	4 53 17	19 27 45	25 58 11	9 8.6	24 14.9	9 42.0	8 8.9	15 58.6	28 49.3	24 55.7	8 12.8	15 56.1
29 Tu	14 30 35	5 53 12	2♌34 10	9♌16 5	9R 8.9	25 55.1	9 6.3	8 47.2	16 5.1	28 47.4	24 55.3	8 13.1	15 58.0
30 W	14 34 31	6 53 9	16 4 12	22 58 45	9 7.8	27 35.2	8 30.1	9 25.6	16 11.5	28 45.4	24 55.1	8 13.4	15 59.8
31 Th	14 38 28	7 53 9	29 59 46	7♍ 7 12	9 5.3	29 15.3	7 53.6	10 3.9	16 17.7	28 43.3	24 54.9	8 13.8	16 1.7

*Giving the positions of planets daily at noon, in LONGITUDE Greenwich Mean Time

NOON EPHEMERIS: GMT*

NOVEMBER 2002

Day	Sid.Time	☉	0 hr ☽	Noon ☽	True ☊	☿	♀	♂	♃	♄	♅	♆	♇
1 F	14 42 24	8♏53 10	14♍20 48	21♍40 7	9♊ 1.6	0♏55.2	7♏17.1	10♎42.3	16♌23.7	28♊41.1	24♒54.7	8♒14.1	16♐ 3.6
2 Sa	14 46 21	9 53 14	29 4 34	6♎33 18	8R 57.4	2 35.0	6R 40.8	11 20.7	16 29.6	28R 38.7	24R 54.6	8 14.6	16 5.6
3 Su	14 50 17	10 53 20	14♎ 5 23	21 39 41	8 53.3	4 14.4	6 5.0	11 59.0	16 35.4	28 36.3	24 54.5	8 15.0	16 7.5
4 M	14 54 14	11 53 27	29 14 59	6♏50 2	8 49.9	5 53.6	5 29.8	12 37.4	16 41.0	28 33.8	24D 54.5	8 15.5	16 9.5
5 Tu	14 58 10	12 53 37	14♏23 34	21 54 25	8 47.7	7 32.5	4 55.6	13 15.8	16 46.4	28 31.2	24 54.5	8 16.0	16 11.5
6 W	15 2 7	13 53 48	29 21 27	6♐43 44	8D 46.9	9 11.1	4 22.6	13 54.2	16 51.6	28 28.5	24 54.6	8 16.6	16 13.5
7 Th	15 6 4	14 54 1	14♐ 0 29	21 11 6	8 47.3	10 49.3	3 50.9	14 32.6	16 56.7	28 25.7	24 54.8	8 17.2	16 15.5
8 F	15 10 0	15 54 16	28 15 10	5♑12 27	8 48.5	12 27.1	3 20.7	15 11.1	17 1.6	28 22.8	24 55.0	8 17.8	16 17.5
9 Sa	15 13 57	16 54 32	12♑ 2 53	18 46 33	8 50.0	14 4.6	2 52.2	15 49.5	17 6.4	28 19.8	24 55.2	8 18.5	16 19.6
10 Su	15 17 53	17 54 50	25 23 41	1♒54 36	8 51.4	15 41.8	2 25.6	16 27.9	17 11.0	28 16.7	24 55.5	8 19.2	16 21.6
11 M	15 21 50	18 55 9	8♒19 41	14 39 25	8R 52.1	17 18.6	2 1.0	17 6.3	17 15.4	28 13.5	24 55.9	8 19.9	16 23.7
12 Tu	15 25 46	19 55 30	20 54 19	27 4 54	8 52.0	18 55.1	1 38.6	17 44.7	17 19.6	28 10.3	24 56.3	8 20.6	16 25.8
13 W	15 29 43	20 55 52	3♓11 44	9♓15 21	8 51.0	20 31.2	1 18.3	18 23.2	17 23.7	28 6.9	24 56.7	8 21.4	16 27.9
14 Th	15 33 39	21 56 15	15 16 20	21 15 10	8 49.2	22 7.0	1 0.4	19 1.6	17 27.6	28 3.5	24 57.2	8 22.3	16 30.0
15 F	15 37 36	22 56 39	27 12 23	3♈ 8 27	8 46.9	23 42.6	0 44.9	19 40.0	17 31.3	28 0.0	24 57.8	8 23.1	16 32.2
16 Sa	15 41 33	23 57 5	9♈ 3 50	14 58 55	8 44.4	25 17.8	0 31.7	20 18.5	17 34.8	27 56.4	24 58.4	8 24.0	16 34.3
17 Su	15 45 29	24 57 33	20 54 7	26 49 46	8 42.1	26 52.8	0 21.1	20 56.9	17 38.1	27 52.7	24 59.0	8 24.9	16 36.5
18 M	15 49 26	25 58 2	2♉46 11	8♉43 40	8 40.2	28 27.5	0 12.9	21 35.4	17 41.3	27 49.0	24 59.7	8 25.9	16 38.7
19 Tu	15 53 22	26 58 32	14 42 29	20 42 51	8 39.0	0♐ 1.9	0 7.2	22 13.9	17 44.3	27 45.2	25 0.5	8 26.8	16 40.8
20 W	15 57 19	27 59 4	26 45 0	2♊49 7	8D 38.4	1 36.2	0 4.0	22 52.3	17 47.1	27 41.3	25 1.3	8 27.9	16 43.0
21 Th	16 1 15	28 59 38	8♊55 26	15 4 6	8 38.4	3 10.2	0D 3.3	23 30.8	17 49.7	27 37.3	25 2.1	8 28.9	16 45.2
22 F	16 5 12	0♐ 0 13	21 15 19	27 29 16	8 38.8	4 44.1	0 5.0	24 9.3	17 52.1	27 33.3	25 3.0	8 30.0	16 47.4
23 Sa	16 9 8	1 0 50	3♋46 9	10♋ 6 8	8 39.6	6 17.8	0 9.1	24 47.8	17 54.4	27 29.2	25 4.0	8 31.1	16 49.7
24 Su	16 13 5	2 1 28	16 29 27	22 56 16	8 40.3	7 51.3	0 15.5	25 26.3	17 56.4	27 25.0	25 5.0	8 32.2	16 51.9
25 M	16 17 2	3 2 8	29 26 50	6♌ 1 19	8 40.9	9 24.7	0 24.3	26 4.8	17 58.3	27 20.8	25 6.0	8 33.4	16 54.1
26 Tu	16 20 58	4 2 50	12♌39 56	19 22 51	8 41.3	10 57.9	0 35.4	26 43.3	17 60.0	27 16.5	25 7.2	8 34.6	16 56.4
27 W	16 24 55	5 3 33	26 10 12	3♍ 2 6	8R 41.5	12 31.0	0 48.6	27 21.9	18 1.4	27 12.2	25 8.3	8 35.8	16 58.6
28 Th	16 28 51	6 4 17	9♍58 33	16 59 34	8 41.4	14 4.0	1 4.0	28 0.4	18 2.7	27 7.8	25 9.5	8 37.1	17 0.9
29 F	16 32 48	7 5 4	24 4 59	1♎14 37	8 41.3	15 36.9	1 21.4	28 38.9	18 3.8	27 3.3	25 10.8	8 38.4	17 3.2
30 Sa	16 36 44	8 5 51	8♎28 7	15 45 3	8 41.2	17 9.8	1 40.9	29 17.5	18 4.7	26 58.8	25 12.1	8 39.7	17 5.4

LONGITUDE

DECEMBER 2002

Day	Sid.Time	☉	0 hr ☽	Noon ☽	True ☊	☿	♀	♂	♃	♄	♅	♆	♇
1 Su	16 40 41	9♐ 6 41	23♎ 4 51	0♏26 52	8♊41.2	18♐42.5	2♏ 2.3	29♎56.1	18♌ 5.4	26♊54.3	25♒13.4	8♒41.0	17♐ 7.7
2 M	16 44 37	10 7 31	7♏50 19	15 14 22	8D 41.3	20 15.1	2 25.6	0♏34.6	18 5.9	26R 49.7	25 14.8	8 42.4	17 10.0
3 Tu	16 48 34	11 8 23	22 38 7	0♐ 0 38	8 41.4	21 47.6	2 50.7	1 13.2	18 6.2	26 45.0	25 16.2	8 43.8	17 12.3
4 W	16 52 31	12 9 17	7♐21 2	14 38 24	8R 41.4	23 20.0	3 17.5	1 51.8	18R 6.3	26 40.3	25 17.7	8 45.2	17 14.5
5 Th	16 56 27	13 10 11	21 51 58	29 1 0	8 41.2	24 52.2	3 46.1	2 30.3	18 6.2	26 35.6	25 19.3	8 46.7	17 16.8
6 F	17 0 24	14 11 7	6♑ 4 54	13♑ 3 13	8 40.7	26 24.4	4 16.2	3 8.9	18 5.9	26 30.9	25 20.9	8 48.2	17 19.1
7 Sa	17 4 20	15 12 3	19 55 37	26 41 56	8 40.0	27 56.3	4 47.9	3 47.5	18 5.4	26 26.1	25 22.5	8 49.7	17 21.4
8 Su	17 8 17	16 13 0	3♒22 5	9♒56 9	8 39.1	29 28.1	5 21.1	4 26.1	18 4.7	26 21.3	25 24.2	8 51.2	17 23.7
9 M	17 12 13	17 13 58	16 24 21	22 46 57	8 38.1	0♑59.6	5 55.7	5 4.7	18 3.8	26 16.4	25 25.9	8 52.8	17 26.0
10 Tu	17 16 10	18 14 56	29 4 21	5♓16 59	8 37.4	2 30.8	6 31.7	5 43.3	18 2.7	26 11.6	25 27.7	8 54.4	17 28.3
11 W	17 20 6	19 15 55	11♓25 21	17 30 1	8D 37.1	4 1.7	7 9.1	6 21.9	18 1.4	26 6.7	25 29.5	8 56.0	17 30.6
12 Th	17 24 3	20 16 55	23 31 34	29 30 35	8 37.3	5 32.2	7 47.7	7 0.5	17 59.9	26 1.8	25 31.4	8 57.6	17 32.9
13 F	17 28 0	21 17 55	5♈27 39	11♈23 24	8 38.0	7 2.1	8 27.6	7 39.1	17 58.3	25 56.8	25 33.3	8 59.3	17 35.2
14 Sa	17 31 56	22 18 55	17 18 24	23 13 15	8 39.2	8 31.5	9 8.7	8 17.7	17 56.4	25 51.9	25 35.2	9 0.9	17 37.5
15 Su	17 35 53	23 19 56	29 8 28	5♉ 4 35	8 40.6	10 0.1	9 50.9	8 56.3	17 54.3	25 47.0	25 37.2	9 2.7	17 39.8
16 M	17 39 49	24 20 58	11♉ 2 5	17 1 25	8 41.9	11 27.9	10 34.3	9 34.9	17 52.1	25 42.0	25 39.2	9 4.4	17 42.1
17 Tu	17 43 46	25 22 0	23 2 59	29 7 8	8 42.9	12 54.6	11 18.7	10 13.5	17 49.6	25 37.1	25 41.3	9 6.1	17 44.3
18 W	17 47 42	26 23 3	5♊14 10	11♊24 21	8R 43.1	14 20.0	12 4.1	10 52.1	17 47.0	25 32.1	25 43.4	9 7.9	17 46.6
19 Th	17 51 39	27 24 7	17 37 52	23 54 53	8 42.4	15 44.0	12 50.5	11 30.8	17 44.1	25 27.2	25 45.6	9 9.7	17 48.9
20 F	17 55 36	28 25 11	0♋15 28	6♋39 41	8 40.7	17 6.2	13 37.9	12 9.4	17 41.1	25 22.3	25 47.8	9 11.5	17 51.2
21 Sa	17 59 32	29 26 15	13 7 32	19 38 57	8 38.1	18 26.3	14 26.2	12 48.0	17 37.9	25 17.3	25 50.0	9 13.4	17 53.4
22 Su	18 3 29	0♑27 21	26 13 52	2♌52 11	8 34.8	19 44.0	15 15.3	13 26.7	17 34.5	25 12.4	25 52.3	9 15.2	17 55.7
23 M	18 7 25	1 28 26	9♌33 45	16 18 26	8 31.2	20 58.8	16 5.3	14 5.3	17 30.9	25 7.5	25 54.6	9 17.1	17 57.9
24 Tu	18 11 22	2 29 33	23 6 4	29 56 29	8 28.0	22 10.2	16 56.1	14 44.0	17 27.2	25 2.6	25 56.9	9 19.0	18 0.2
25 W	18 15 18	3 30 40	6♍49 33	13♍45 4	8 25.6	23 17.7	17 47.7	15 22.6	17 23.2	24 57.7	25 59.3	9 20.9	18 2.4
26 Th	18 19 15	4 31 47	20 42 54	27 42 54	8 24.3	24 20.6	18 40.1	16 1.3	17 19.1	24 52.9	26 1.8	9 22.9	18 4.6
27 F	18 23 11	5 32 56	4♎44 53	11♎48 41	8D 24.3	25 18.3	19 33.2	16 40.0	17 14.8	24 48.1	26 4.2	9 24.8	18 6.8
28 Sa	18 27 8	6 34 5	18 54 6	26 0 56	8 25.3	26 9.9	20 26.9	17 18.7	17 10.3	24 43.3	26 6.7	9 26.8	18 9.1
29 Su	18 31 5	7 35 14	3♏ 8 56	10♏17 48	8 26.8	26 54.7	21 21.4	17 57.3	17 5.7	24 38.5	26 9.3	9 28.8	18 11.3
30 M	18 35 1	8 36 24	17 27 11	24 36 43	8 28.2	27 31.7	22 16.5	18 36.0	17 0.9	24 33.7	26 11.8	9 30.8	18 13.4
31 Tu	18 38 58	9 37 34	1♐45 56	8♐54 23	8R 28.8	28 0.1	23 12.1	19 14.7	16 55.9	24 29.0	26 14.4	9 32.8	18 15.6

*Giving the positions of planets daily at noon,
in LONGITUDE Greenwich Mean Time

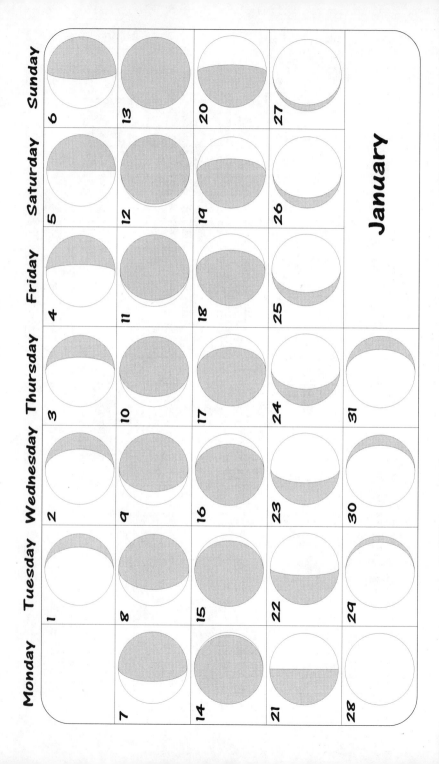

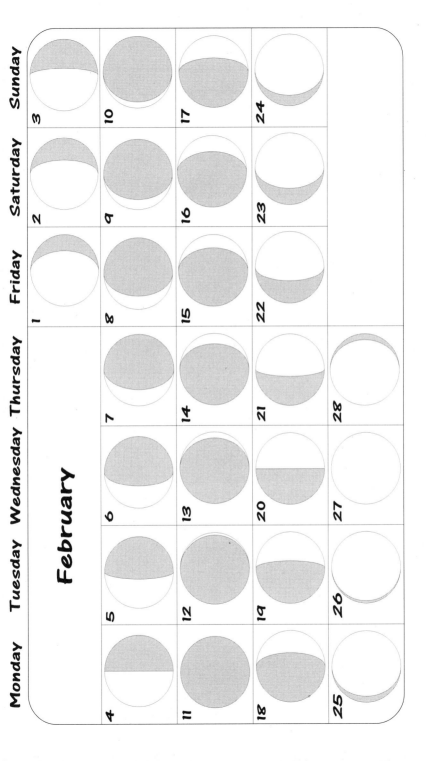

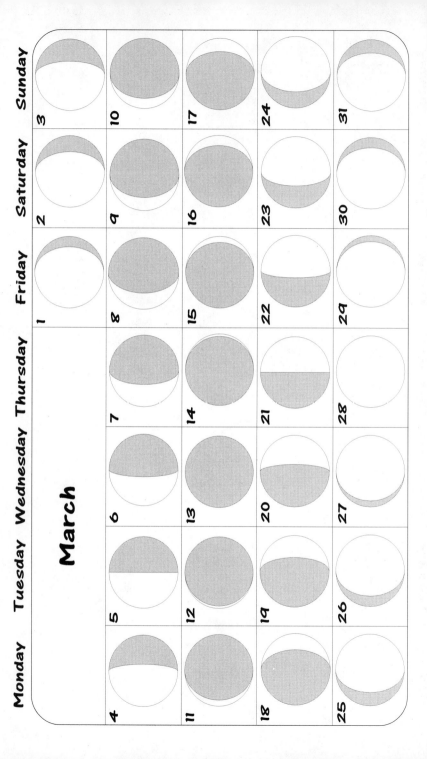

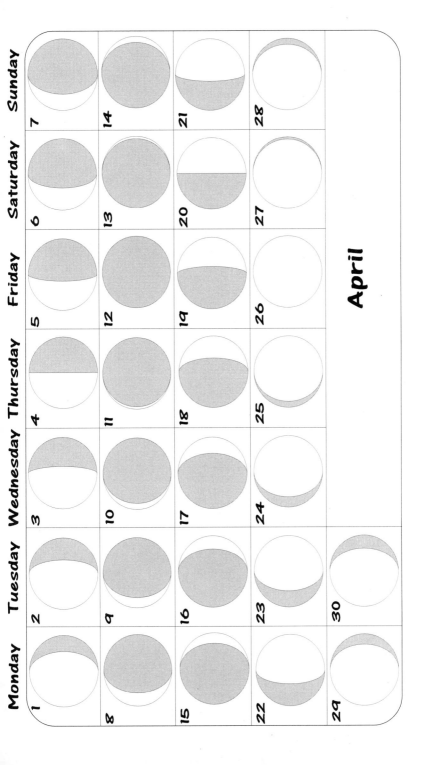

April

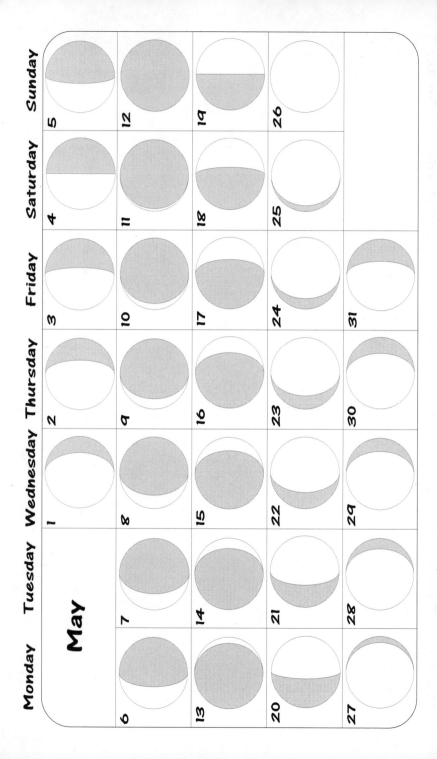

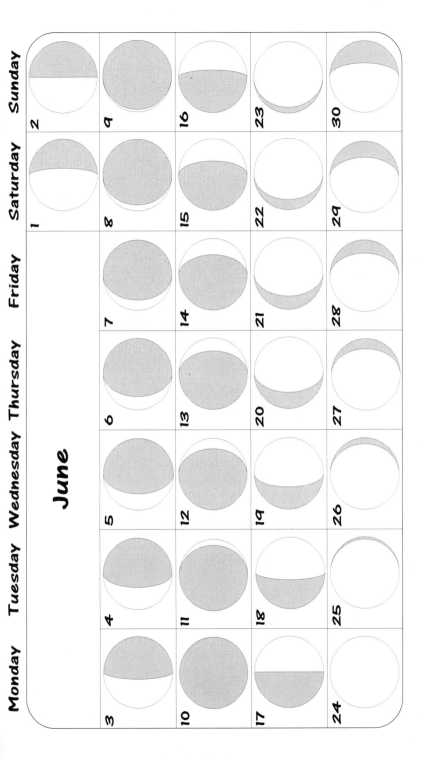

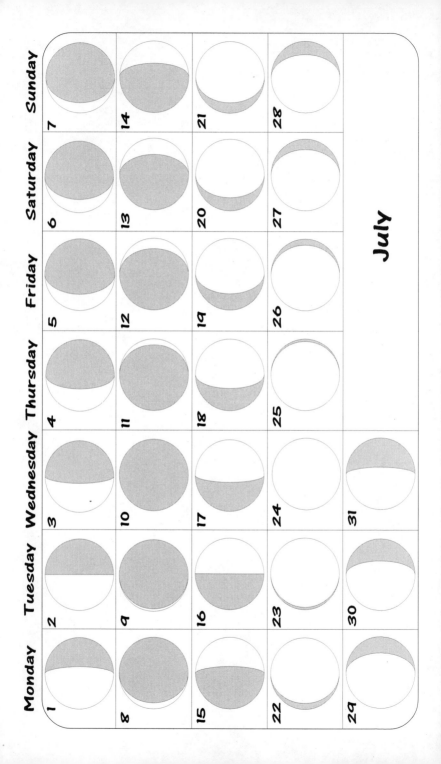

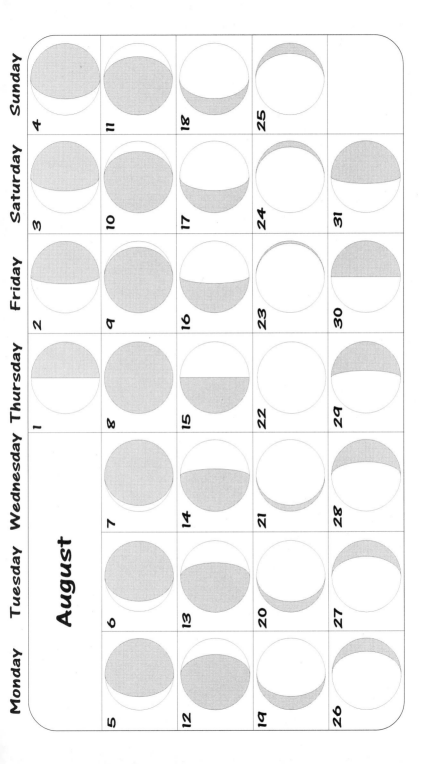

August

Monday	Tuesday	Wednesday	Thursday	Friday	Saturday	Sunday
			1	2	3	4
5	6	7	8	9	10	11
12	13	14	15	16	17	18
19	20	21	22	23	24	25
26	27	28	29	30	31	

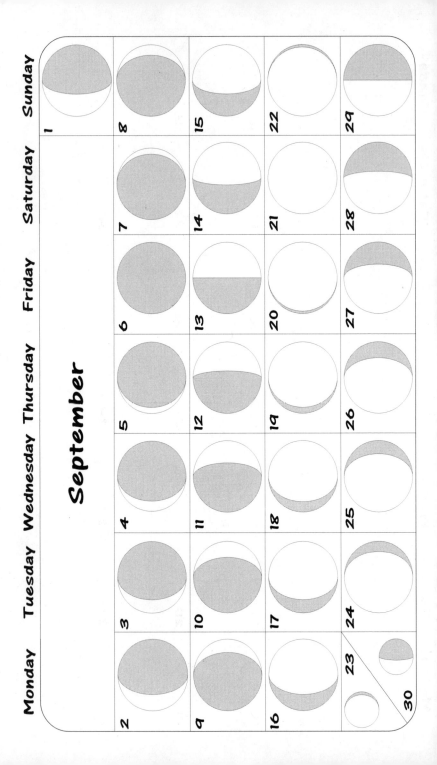

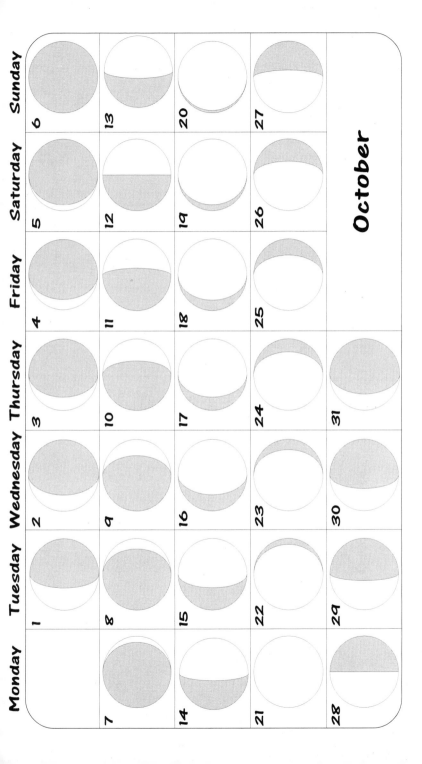

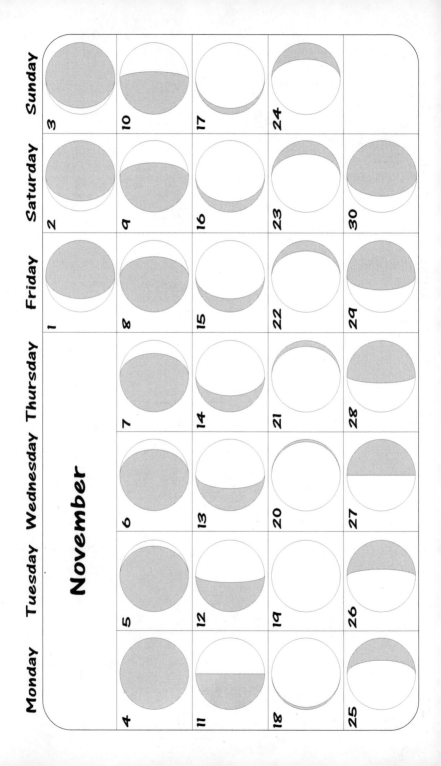

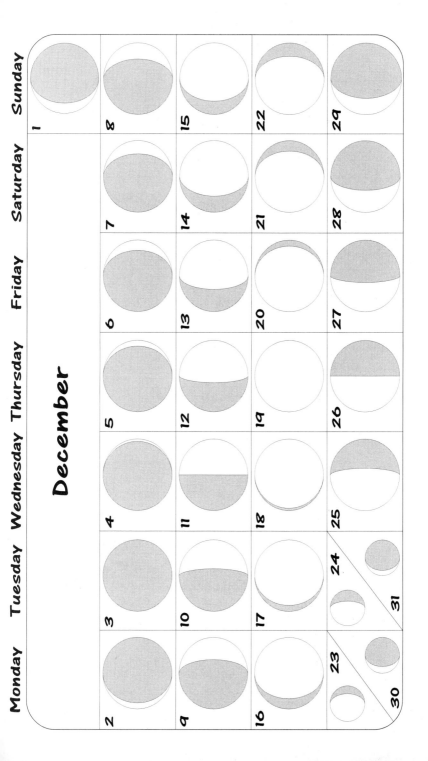

WORLD TIME ZONES

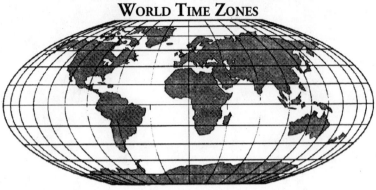

ID LW	NT BT	CA HT	YST	PST	MST	CST	EST	AST	BST	AT	WAT	GMT	CET	EET	BT	USSR Z3	USSR Z4	USSR Z5	SST	CCT	JST	GST	USSR Z10	ID LE
-12	-11	-10	-9	-8	-7	-6	-5	-4	-3	-2	-1	0	+1	+2	+3	+4	+5	+6	+7	+8	+9	+10	+11	+12
-4	-3	-2	-1	0	+1	+2	+3	+4	+5	+6	+7	+8	+9	+10	+11	+12	+13	+14	+15	+16	+17	+18	+19	+20

STANDARD TIME ZONES FROM WEST TO EAST CALCULATED FROM PST AS ZERO POINT:

IDLW:	International Date Line West	-4
NT/BT:	Nome Time/Bering Time	-3
CA/HT:	Central Alaska & Hawaiian Time	-2
YST:	Yukon Standard Time	-1
PST:	Pacific Standard Time	0
MST:	Mountain Standard Time	+1
CST:	Central Standard Time	+2
EST:	Eastern Standard Time	+3
AST:	Atlantic Standard Time	+4
NFT:	Newfoundland Time	+4 1/2
BST:	Brazil Standard Time	+5
AT:	Azores Time	+6
WAT:	West African Time	+7
GMT:	Greenwich Mean Time	+8
WET:	Western European Time (England)	+8
CET:	Central European Time	+9
EET:	Eastern European Time	+10
BT:	Bagdhad Time	+11
IT:	Iran Time	+11 1/2
USSR	Zone 3	+12
USSR	Zone 4	+13
IST:	Indian Standard Time	+13 1/2
USSR	Zone 5	+14
NST:	North Sumatra Time	+14 1/2
SST:	South Sumatra Time & USSR Zone 6	+15
JT:	Java Time	+15 1/2
CCT:	China Coast Time	+16
MT:	Moluccas Time	+16 1/2
JST:	Japanese Standard Time	+17
SAST:	South Australian Standard Time	+17 1/2
GST:	Guam Standard Time	+18
USSR	Zone 10	+19
IDLE:	International Date Line East	+20

HOW TO CALCULATE TIME ZONE CORRECTIONS IN YOUR AREA:

ADD if you are **east** of PST (Pacific Standard Time); **SUBTRACT** if you are **west** of PST on this map (see right-hand column of chart above).

All times in this calendar are calculated from the West Coast of North America where it is made. Pacific Standard Time (PST Zone 8) is zero point for this calendar except during Daylight Savings Time (April 7– October 27, 2002 during which times are given for PDT Zone 7). If your time zone does not use Daylight Savings Time, add one hour to the standard correction during this time. At the bottom of each page EST/ EDT (Eastern Standard or Daylight Time) and GMT (Greenwich Mean Time) times are also given. For all other time zones, calculate your time zone correction(s) from this map and write it on the inside cover for easy reference.

SIGNS AND SYMBOLS AT A GLANCE

PLANETS

Personal Planets are closest to Earth.

⊙ **Sun**: self radiating outward, character, ego
☽ **Moon**: inward sense of self, emotions, psyche
☿ **Mercury**: communication, travel, thought
♀ **Venus**: relationship, love, sense of beauty, empathy
♂ **Mars**: will to act, initiative, ambition

Asteroids are between Mars and Jupiter and reflect the awakening of feminine-defined energy centers in human consciousness. See "Asteroids" (p.199).

Social Planets are between personal and outer planets.

♃ **Jupiter**: expansion, opportunities, leadership
♄ **Saturn**: limits, structure, discipline

Note: the seven days of the week are named after the above seven heavenly bodies.

⚷ **Chiron**: is a small planetary body between Saturn and Uranus representing the wounded healer.

Transpersonal Planets are the outer planets.

♅ **Uranus**: cosmic consciousness, revolutionary change
♆ **Neptune**: spiritual awakening, cosmic love, all one
♇ **Pluto**: death and rebirth, deep, total change

ZODIAC SIGNS

♈	Aries
♉	Taurus
♊	Gemini
♋	Cancer
♌	Leo
♍	Virgo
♎	Libra
♏	Scorpio
♐	Sagittarius
♑	Capricorn
♒	Aquarius
♓	Pisces

ASPECTS

Aspects show the angle between planets; this informs how the planets influence each other and us. **We'Moon** lists only significant aspects:

♂ CONJUNCTION (planets are 0–5° apart)
   linked together, energy of aspected planets is mutually enhancing
✶ SEXTILE (planets are 60° apart)
   cooperative, energies of this aspect blend well
□ SQUARE (planets are 90° apart)
   challenging, energies of this aspect are different from each other
△ TRINE (planets are 120° apart)
   harmonizing, energies of this aspect are in the same element
☍ OPPOSITION (planets are 180° apart)
   polarizing or complementing, energies are diametrically opposite
⚻ QUINCUNX (planets are 150° apart)
   variable, energies of this aspect combine contrary elements

OTHER SYMBOLS

☽ **v/c:** Moon is void of course from last lunar aspect till it enters new sign.
ApG–Apogee: Point in the orbit of a planet that's farthest from Earth.
PrG–Perigee: Point in the orbit of a planet that's nearest to Earth.
D or R–Direct or Retrograde: Describes when a planet moves forward (D) through the zodiac or appears to move backward (R).

DEF

GHI

JKL

MNO

PQR

STU